ARABIC   ASTRONOMY   BANKING   BEE-KEEPING
NISATION   CALCULUS   CAN
MMERCIAL CORRESPONDENCE
NG   CRICKET   DRAWING
ELECTRICITY IN THE HOUSE   EMBROIDERY
ENGLISH RENASCENCE TO THE ROMANTIC REVIVAL   ROMANTIC
ERYDAY FRENCH   TO EXPRESS YOURSELF   FISHING   TO FLY
BOOK   GARDENING   GAS IN THE HOUSE   GEOGRAPHY OF
NARY   GERMAN GRAMMAR   GERMAN PHRASE BOOK   GOLF
GOOD FARM ACCOUNTING   GOOD FARM CROPS   GOOD FARMING
FARMING.   GOOD GRASSLAND   GOOD AND HEALTHY ANIMALS
GOOD POULTRY KEEPING   GOOD SHEEP FARMING   GOOD SOIL
HINDUSTANI   HISTORY: ABRAHAM LINCOLN ALEXANDER THE
CONSTANTINE   COOK   CRANMER   ERASMUS   GLADSTONE AND
TON   PERICLES   PETER THE GREAT   PUSHKIN   RALEIGH   RICHELIEU
ROW   EMENT
AN   LETTER
NGIN   ANICS
ERN   · · · · AND HE WILL BE   ORING
LOSO   HYSICS
UMBI   YET WISER *Proverbs 9.9*   UBLIC
ECKO   USSIAN
ITS N   AND PURPOSE   SOCCER   SPANISH   SPE   AND
SW   SWEDISH   TEACHING   THINKING   TRIG   METRY
BRI   H RAILWAYS FOR BOYS   CAMPING FOR BOYS AND GIRLS
R GIRLS   MODELMAKING FOR BOYS   NEEDLEWORK FOR GIRLS
S AND GIRLS   SAILING AND SMALL BOATS FOR BOYS AND GIRLS
K FOR BOYS   ADVERTISING & PUBLICITY   ALGEBRA   AMATEUR
G   BIOLOGY   BOOK-KEEPING   BRICKWORK   BRINGING UP
RY   CHEMISTRY   CHESS   CHINESE   COMMERCIAL ARITHMETIC
AVELLING   TO COMPOSE MUSIC   CONSTRUCTIONAL DETAILS
DUTCH   DUTTON SPEEDWORDS   ECONOMIC GEOGRAPHY
EMBROIDERY   ENGLISH GRAMMAR   LITERARY APPRECIATION
AL   ROMANTIC REVIVAL   VICTORIAN AGE   CONTEMPORARY
ISHING   TO FLY   FREELANCE WRITING   FRENCH   FRENCH
SE   GEOGRAPHY OF LIVING THINGS   GEOLOGY   GEOMETRY
E BOOK   GOLF   GOOD CONTROL OF INSECT PESTS   GOOD
RM CROPS   GOOD FARMING   GOOD FARMING BY MACHINE
GOOD AND HEALTHY ANIMALS   GOOD MARKET GARDENING
GOOD SHEEP FARMING   GOOD SOIL   GOOD ENGLISH   GREEK
Y: ABRAHAM LINCOLN   ALEXANDER THE GREAT BOLIVAR   BOTHA
ANMER   ERASMUS   GLADSTONE AND LIBERALISM   HENRY V   JOAN OF
PUSHKIN   RALEIGH   RICHELIEU   ROBESPIERRE   THOMAS JEFFERSON
OME NURSING   HORSE MANAGEMENT   HOUSEHOLD DOCTOR
RNALISM   LATIN   LAWN TENNIS   LETTER WRITER   MALAY
NENTS   WORKSHOP PRACTICE   MECHANICS   MECHANICAL
MORE GERMAN   MOTHERCRAFT   MOTORING   MOTOR CYCLING
HY   PHYSICAL GEOGRAPHY   PHYSICS   PHYSIOLOGY   PITMAN'S
SE   PSYCHOLOGY   PUBLIC ADMINISTRATION   PUBLIC SPEAKING

THE TEACH YOURSELF BOOKS
EDITED BY LEONARD CUTTS

TEACH YOURSELF
TO FLY

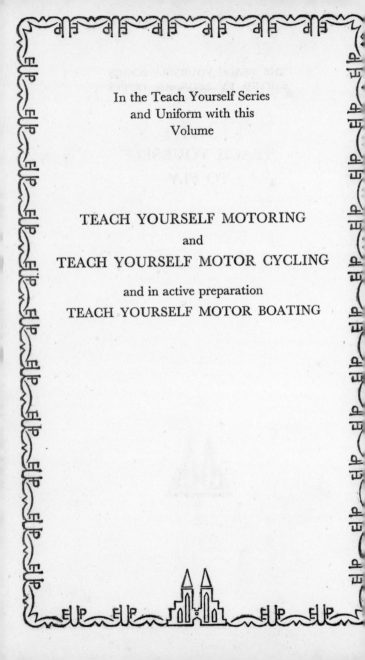

TEACH YOURSELF
TO FLY

Originally planned and written by
NIGEL TANGYE
now fully revised, re-written, and
brought up to date by
D. H. MacBEATH
and edited by THE GUILD OF AIR
PILOTS AND AIR NAVIGATORS OF
THE BRITISH EMPIRE

ENGLISH UNIVERSITIES PRESS LTD.
LONDON

First Printed 1938
Reprinted 1950
Completely Revised 1952

Printed in Great Britain for the English Universities Press, Limited,
by Richard Clay and Company, Ltd., Bungay, Suffolk.

PREFACE

THE original edition of this book *Teach Yourself to Fly*, so ably written by Nigel Tangye, has for a number of years filled a long-felt want. It was much sought after by those keen young people—of both sexes—whose interest in aviation was aroused; and particularly by those who, having already made up their minds to learn to fly at the first opportunity, were wise enough to find out all they could about the art before facing their first practical flying lesson.

I think the publishers are to be congratulated on their wisdom in deciding that a book of this kind—dealing with a rapidly progressing art—must be re-written and brought up to date from time to time, if it is to retain its eminence.

The Guild of Air Pilots and Air Navigators of the British Empire feels it was paid a compliment when the publishers invited it to undertake this task.

The Guild had no hesitation in accepting this request, for it considers it has special qualifications to do so. As long ago as 1931 the Guild introduced its Panel of Examiners. This Panel, composed of a number of very experienced flying instructors, undertakes the examination of flying instructors, and if necessary, the testing or re-testing of their capabilities. The Panel of

Examiners was subsequently ratified by the Ministry of Civil Aviation, and is now the authorised body for the testing of instructors' competence, and it is on their recommendation that the Ministry grant a pilot an Instructor's Rating on his licence.

It is to Mr. Donald H. MacBeath and the Panel of Examiners that we are indebted for the considerable work involved in bringing this book *Teach Yourself to Fly* up to date and in line with the latest instructional technique. Mr. MacBeath has served as a member of the Court of the Guild, and is himself a successful and experienced flying instructor, and a recipient of His Late Majesty the King's Commendation for good work during the war.

Although many years have passed since I had need of such a book, for it was in 1913 that I learned to fly on a Vickers Boxkite under that great instructor, the late Harold Barnwell, I have read the latest version from cover to cover with the greatest possible interest and indeed not without some queer nostalgic feelings. May it assist and bring good luck to the rising generation as much as I am sure it would have helped and thrilled me in those far-off Brooklands days.

J. LANKESTER PARKER, O.B.E., F.R.Ae.S.
Master of the Guild 1951–52.

CONTENTS

LIST OF PLATES

INTRODUCTION

FOUR years before I had an opportunity to be flown in an aeroplane, I started to learn to fly. A few months later, when I had studied every text-book on the subject that I could find, I passed myself out in my mind as a fully qualified pilot. From then on, whenever I had a leisure moment, I would take flight in my mind with the most modern aeroplanes. Sometimes I would climb into the still evening air in a single-seat fighter and have a glorious half-hour of aerobatics. Sometimes, when the weather was rough and forbidding, I would take my place as second pilot beside the captain of an air-liner on a regular air route, intent on maintaining a schedule. And sometimes I would take a rest from flying a land-plane and in my fancy try a flying-boat, and change its element from blue water to blue sky by opening the throttles of its engines and coaxing it into the air, silver and shining in the sun. All this I did in my mind. All this I did with scrupulous attention to control movement, to engine temperatures and pressures, to wind strength and direction, to petrol consumption—in fact, to everything that a pilot has to keep track of as he speeds into the air and ranges across the sky. With the confidence of youth, I would have accepted the invitation of any pilot to take his machine into the air, so sure was I that my studies and my many flights in fancy had taught me all that was necessary for a pilot to know.

It was not until many years later that I had my first real lesson, and within a few minutes of being in the air I discovered, to my dismay, that, by some curious oversight at the very beginning of my self-instruction, I would have come to grief on my first flight in fancy. But that mistake was soon rectified by my instructor, and I can truthfully say that, quite apart from the many happy hours of make-believe I had piloting an aeroplane, the study that I had made of flying saved a lot of instruction that I would otherwise have needed before I was sent on my first solo. It is because of this experience, no less because of the enjoyment that lies in the study of flying by the enthusiast, that I have undertaken to write this book.

The title, *Teach Yourself to Fly*, I do not intend to be taken literally. However confident the reader may feel when he has reached the last page, he must appreciate that the putting into practice of what he has read will take a little time, but if this book is used as a basis to augment the instruction given in the air, an enormous amount of the fundamentals of flying will be more readily understood.

In this book I have not attempted to touch on any evolution that cannot be made in a normal training aircraft. The machine I have had in my mind's eye is the orthodox monoplane at present used as the basic trainer of the Royal Air Force, fitted with an air-cooled engine of 140 horse-power, which gives it a speed of about 100 knots. The two seats are arranged in tandem—that is, one behind the other—with the instructor sitting in the rear. Electrical intercommunication is now the normal practice for conversation between the instructor and pupil, but speaking tubes are still used in most Club machines.

If I introduced machines that were equipped with the various appendages and devices, such as variable-pitch propellers, constant-pitch propellers, retractable undercarriages, and tricycle under-carriages, the lessons would become too complicated for a clear picture of flying to remain in the mind of the reader. All these devices have appeared in the last few years, and so complicated have aero-planes other than training machines become, that even experienced pilots have to study the instru-ment panel and controls for half an hour or so before they feel ready to take the machine up for the first time. Gone are those happy, carefree days when a new type of aeroplane would appear out of the sky and land on the aerodrome, and the pilot would come over to you and say, " Like to try her? " There are, alas! too many gadgets about an aeroplane now for a pilot to feel so confidently generous.

Another point about this book I should explain is the sequence of instruction I have followed. When you actually learn to fly, you will, for instance, be taught to fly straight and level before you learn to take off. In this book, for interest's sake, I have gone straight through the sequence of events that face a pilot from the time he gets into his aeroplane to the time he gets out of the cockpit after his flight.

You will gain considerable assistance for your study of this book if you take a passenger flight in an aeroplane before you start reading it. If you are in the Air Training Corps, such an opportunity will come your way. Seize it with both hands. This experience will make everything easier for you to appreciate, because in your mind you will be able to have a realistic background of what it feels like to fly and what the earth looks like far below you; and you will have the satisfaction of learning that when you are in an aeroplane there is no sensation of giddiness, as when you are looking over the parapet of a high building. You view the earth, which lies perhaps thousands of feet below you, with a feeling of complete detachment and, unless you are a very nervous type, of security—so long as you have not chosen as your pilot a friend who thinks it a good opportunity to " show off ". More people have been put off flying by wrongly choosing the circumstances of their first flight than by any other cause. An experienced pilot knows that when he is taking up a passenger on his first flight, the novelty of flying is quite enough to make him appreciatively impressed by the pilot's capabilities. He does not wish to be thrown about the sky, as is so often done by the young and arrogant pilot who is taking a friend up for a first flight. If he does throw his plane about

under these circumstances, you may be pretty
sure he is doing it badly into the bargain, so that
you are doubly advised to keep clear of him. A
good pilot just simply will not do it, unless you
specifically ask him to—in which case he will do
some of the more gentle evolutions, and be ready
to stop the instant he sees you begin to look a bit
green.

No, on principle, keep clear of your friends for
your introduction to the air. When you know
something about flying you will be able to judge
their ability for yourself. You can then make
whatever use you can of them, provided they
satisfy you that they are safe!

When your pilot has helped you into your cockpit and climbs into his own, you will inevitably
feel a little tense. To your unpractised eye the
machine will appear to be a frail craft in which to
entrust your life by being taken up into the air at
a hundred miles an hour. Remember that an
aeroplane is the strongest machine for its weight
that has ever been built by man, and take comfort
accordingly. Relax. Loosen your muscles and sit
quite calmly in your seat. Physical relaxation is
almost the paramount pre-requisite in learning to
fly. It is the secret of enjoying flying from the
first moment that you sit in an aeroplane. The
pilot will taxi the machine out into the best
position on the aerodrome for the take-off, which
normally will be made into wind. As it trundles
over the uneven ground, you will be " bounced "
about a bit, though the " bounces " are in fact

exaggerated. Do not worry. As soon as your pilot opens his throttle and the plane starts to get airborne, this " bouncing " will diminish, until, when the wheels leave the ground, it will have stopped altogether, and you are climbing smoothly into the sky, the earth speeding beneath your wing-tips and fading farther and farther away. On certain days, either when it is very hot weather or windy, the air will be a little bumpy. You will feel the plane rising and dropping in small, sudden movements. If this happens your instinct will play you false and your muscles will tauten. Again you must apply the golden rule and relax. You will then find the bumps are not at all frightening.

Incidentally, your instinct will often play you false when flying. Treat it as a fickle jade, and you will do much better. For instance, when you are flying in cloud by instruments, your instinct will often all but persuade you that your instruments are lying. They show you to be flying straight, but your instinct shouts in your ear, louder and louder, that you are turning to the left. Be strong, and pay no attenton to its voice. Your instruments will be right. And when you have been flying on a compass course for some time over country on which you have been unable to pick out a landmark, the voice of your instinct will start whispering in your ear that your compass is wrong. It will soon be shouting in your ear that the compass is leading you too far to the right. No wonder you cannot pick up the expected landmark. But pay no attention to your instinct on such an occasion. Trust your compass.

When you get into the air, take a good look round you, and try to imprint in your memory what you see and what you feel, so that when you get down you have more than just an " amusement-park " experience to remember. Look at the ground beneath you and see what landmarks stand out most. Notice how clear is the pattern of roadways, and how marked is the tenuous line of the railway. See how woods form well-defined shapes (but bear in mind that the need for timber during the War years may have seriously altered their shape), likewise lakes or reservoirs. These are the sort of landmarks which the pilot uses to find his way, by fitting their pattern on his map to the life-size pattern on the ground.

You will not be in the air long before your pilot does a turn. Unless you know what is happening this is apt to be rather an alarming experience. If he turns to the left, your left wing will dip and your right wing rise, until the whole aeroplane is banked to the left and it starts to turn. Do not obey the instinct which will influence you to lean outwards from the turn. Treat it for what it is— a fickle jade—and pay no attention, but sit quite naturally in the seat. However far the pilot banks the plane, you will find that there is no tendency for you to fall out.

Try to persuade the pilot, before you go up, to fly above the clouds, for this is an experience you will never forget. Maybe on the day you choose for your first flight there will be no clouds, or perhaps they will be too high for the pilot to reach. But ask him to take you to them if it is humanly possible. The inside of a cloud is no different from a thick fog. The wings of your plane stretch into it on either side of you, their tips nearly obscured, and you feel as though you are quite still. Only the roar of the engine and the needle of the air-speed indicator will tell you that you are flying at 100 knots. As the aeroplane climbs up through it, the bleak unfriendliness of the fog becomes brighter, until, just before the plane breaks through the top, the white glare around you strains your eyes. Then all of a sudden you are clear of it, and you find yourself in a dazzling firmament of sunshine, an unbroken surface of glistening snow beneath you and a limitless bowl of blue sky above. Cut off from the world of reality, you are suspended in a world of fantasy which the most virile imagination could not picture to its full extent. And perhaps as impressive as anything is the perfect smoothness of the air in which you fly, for there are rarely air currents to disturb the serenity of even flight above the clouds.

The return through the clouds is as depressing as the climb is exhilarating. The eye has become accustomed to the vital splendour of the sun and sky, with the result that the air-space between cloud and earth appears to be gloom personified. But after a few minutes the eye once more attunes itself to the sunless light, and the gloom disappears.

You may have a slight shock, on this first flight of yours, when the even note of the engine suddenly stops and there is silence, except for the swish of wind over wing and fuselage. Be prepared for this, and it will not disturb you. It is only the pilot throttling back the engine to start his glide down to the aerodrome. In order to lose height, he does not need his engine—rather in the same way when you are coasting down a hill in a car, the force of gravity is quite sufficient to keep you going. Try to pick out the aerodrome as early as possible, so that you can follow the pilot's movement of the plane as he judges his approach to it. It is this part of flying, and the judgment required in landing gently at 50 miles an hour or so, that you will find most difficult to surmount when you are learning.

Throughout this approach, remember the golden rule—I cannot repeat it too often—relax. You may think, as you get near the ground and begin to see the speed at which you are travelling, that the instructor is sure to hit the hedge which bounds the aerodrome. Have no fear. He will clear it all right. Nor is he going to hit the ground with the bump that you expect as the ground rushes a few feet beneath you. You will hardly feel the movement of contact of wheels and ground. Only the change of attitude of the machine as the tail comes down and rests on the ground and the " bouncing " effect of the undercarriage as the aeroplane rolls to a standstill will tell you that you are on earth again.

CHAPTER I

CONTROLS AND INSTRUMENTS

BEFORE you take your first lesson in the air it will be necessary for the various vital parts of the aeroplane to be explained to you. Exercise a little patience, and bear with me while I give you some definitions which it is necessary for me to use in the ensuing pages if I hope to meet with success in translating the movement and sense of flying on to paper.

You have arrived at the aerodrome, met your instructor, and are ready to start on your course of flying. The aeroplane in which you are going to be given your lessons is standing on the tarmac in front of the hangar. It is a low-wing monoplane—that is, an aeroplane with a single wing on which rests the fuselage, so that the floor of the cockpit is roughly on a level with the top surface of the wing.

When you come near to the plane, you will see details which need explaining. Stretching from half-way along the rear edge—called the TRAILING EDGE—to the tips of each wing, is a flap which is hinged to the REAR SPAR (inside the wing, so that you cannot see it) of the wing. These two flaps are AILERONS, and are vital control surfaces. If you lift the right-wing aileron and look over the fuselage to the one on the other wing, you will see that the left-wing aileron goes down; and if you depress the right-wing aileron you will see that the left-wing aileron goes up. This is because they are interconnected at the CONTROL COLUMN in the cockpit. Now walk over to the cockpit and move the control column (often called by pilots the STICK) to the left and right, and at the same time watch the ailerons. If the stick is moved to the left, you will see the left-hand aileron hinge upward and the right-hand aileron hinge downward. Move the stick to the right, and the reverse happens.

This aileron control is the means by which a pilot BANKS his aeroplane from one side to the other, and it happens this way: Suppose he is flying along at 100 knots, and he wishes to lower his left wing; he moves his stick over to the left, and this hinges the left aileron upward. The rush of air over the left wing strikes this aileron, and naturally tries to blow it out of its way. What happens? The aileron is pushed downwards, but because the pilot is holding on to the stick and the aileron is attached to the wing, the wing-tip is pushed downwards. The same thing happens to the other wing in the reverse direction, because the right aileron is depressed and the rushing air pushes the right wing-tip up. The whole aeroplane therefore turns around its LONGITUDINAL AXIS (an imaginary line drawn through the FUSELAGE, or body, from nose to tail) until the pilot centralises the stick and the ailerons return to their original position flush with the wing.

The movement of the plane around its longitudinal axis is helped by the ailerons in another way. Without going into aerodynamical details, the lift of a wing is increased a little by an aileron being depressed and decreased by an aileron being raised. Because of this fact, a wing which is dipped, due to the resistance of its raised aileron to the air-stream, is helped to dip further by the loss of lift to that wing. At the same time the gain in lift of the opposite wing helps the plane to rotate about its longitudinal axis.

The control surface which deals with YAW is the RUDDER. Take a good look at it. You will see that you can move it from side to side in the same way as you can move the ailerons. But instead of being hinged on a horizontal spar, it is hinged on the vertical FIN, which is fixed to the fuselage in the centre of the tailplane. You will see that the rudder has about a 30-degree movement on either side of the centre line of the fuselage. Now go to the cockpit and climb into it. You will find a horizontal bar on which to put your feet. This bar is pivoted about a pin at its centre, and is connected by wires to the rudder in such a way that when you push your left foot forward the rudder is deflected to the left. When in the air the air-stream striking this deflected rudder surface tries to push it out of its way, with the result that the tail of the aeroplane is pushed round and the nose of the plane yaws to the left. Put in its simplest terms, if you want the nose to turn to the left, you push your left foot forward, and to the right, your right foot forward. THE MOVEMENT OF THE PIVOTED "STEERING"-BAR IS THEREFORE JUST THE OPPOSITE TO THE MOVEMENT OF A BICYCLE HANDLE-BAR.

Before you leave the rudder for the time being, take a look at the fin. At first sight this appears to be in line with the centre line of the fuselage, and it serves the obvious function of helping to keep the machine straight. But if you look closely, you will see that it is just a few degrees out of the centre line. This is because the re-volving propeller pushes the air back (it is the reaction to this which pulls the aeroplane forward) in a corkscrew shape, sweeping it back over the fuselage in a spiral. If the fin was built in line with the fuselage the air-stream would strike it at a slight angle all the time, with the result that, far from the fin helping the pilot to keep the machine straight, it would be tending to turn it. To counter this spiral effect, you will observe that the fin is therefore set at the slight angle to the centre line of the fuselage.

You have now been shown the rudder control, which controls yaw, and the aileron controls, which control the banking of the plane around the longitudinal axis. There is one more control to see, and that is the ELEVATOR, which is hinged to the trailing edge of the tailplane on either side of the rudder. This control surface is hinged horizontally, and can therefore be moved up and down. Applying to it exactly the same principle as the action of the air-stream on rudder and ailerons, it is easy to understand that when the elevator is raised the tail of the aeroplane is pushed down by the air-stream, with the result that the aeroplane assumes an attitude in which the nose is higher than when in normal flight. The elevator is attached to the stick in such a manner that when the pilot wishes to climb he eases the stick back, and when he wants to dive he eases it forward.

In all these control movements it is very important to realise that they work only so long as the stick is out of its central position. As soon as the pilot has attained the attitude he desires, then he centralises his stick and the aeroplane will maintain that attitude. There are exceptions to this which will be explained later, but in principle that is what happens.

While you are looking at the tail unit (Plate II), a refinement must be explained to you. It is easy to understand that under various conditions of load an aeroplane will be out of balance. In other words, it will not tend, without constant attention by the pilot, to fly level, as it should do. This may happen when a heavy pilot has been flying the aeroplane in perfect trim and the next man to take it up is light in weight. Under such conditions it is reasonable to understand that the aeroplane is out of trim for the light-weight pilot. The nose of the machine will either tend to drop or rise, according to the change of position of the centre of gravity of the machine occasioned by the different weight of the two

pilots. Suppose the nose tended to drop—in
other words, the machine was NOSE HEAVY (the
opposite inclination is TAIL HEAVY)—the pilot
would have to exert pressure on the stick in order
to keep the elevators in the " up " position all the
time he required to fly level. This is very undesirable. In your training aircraft you will see a
wheel which works the elevator trim, or more
popularly the TAIL TRIM (Plate III), and, according
to the position it is set, it increases or decreases the
load on the stick. The pilot can therefore set it
to the position that allows him to fly the aeroplane
comfortably, irrespective of the disposition of the
loading, providing, of course, that the limits for
the type are not exceeded.

A moment's thought, and you will see that the
three controls that I have just explained allow a
pilot complete freedom of movement in the air.
Various combinations of all three enable him to
put his machine in whatever attitude he likes.
When you have got this quite clear in your mind
(a model cut out in paper will enable you to
grasp it), go back to the cockpit and have a look
at the instrument panel (Plate III).

In training machines of earlier days the minimum of instruments were provided, and as a
pilot graduated on to other types he became con-
fronted with an array of dials he had never seen
before. The practice nowadays is to familiarise
the pupil with at least the essential instruments
from the word go, and so the cockpit of a modern
trainer takes on much of the appearance of a

single-seater fighter. I am going fairly thoroughly into the functioning of each instrument, and although this may seem to be a little tedious at this stage, its benefit will become apparent later on.

We will be going into the air together soon, and with regard to the instruments, there is one word of warning I would like to give. Try to overcome the desire to give your instruments undue attention. In the early stages it is far more important to be aware of what is going on outside the cockpit than what is going on inside. The attitude of the aeroplane, the position of the nose, the level of the wings are much more important to you during this time than is the functioning of the artificial horizon, and, above all, it is most important to keep an alert look-out all round you, and this cannot be done with your head in the cockpit.

We will now consider each instrument as it appears in Plate III, starting with the top left-hand corner.

The engine revolution counter, or more correctly tachometer, is an instrument which records the number of the crankshaft revolutions of the engine per minute, and this is directly controlled by the throttle.

The air-speed indicator is an instrument operated by air pressure in an aneroid capsule. Pressure is admitted to the aneroid capsule by a pressure, or dynamic, tube, and ordinary atmospheric pressure is maintained around the capsule by the static tube. As the aircraft moves through the air a greater pressure of air forces its way into the pressure tube, thereby distending the capsule against the static pressure. The amount of the distention is converted by linkage to give a reading on the dial. The other ends of the pressure and static tubes are taken to what is known as the Pitot head, which has probably already excited your attention (Plate IV). The Pitot (pronounced PEETO) head is the curious contraption that looks like two pencils mounted well out on the wing. If you examine it closely you will notice that one "pencil" has an open end (the pressure tube) and the other has a series of fine holes drilled in it (the static tube). The positioning of the Pitot head is of extreme importance, as, if for instance, it was mounted in the slip-stream of the propeller, a highly fictitious reading would be the result. Most A.S.I.s are now calibrated in knots, as the nautical mile (you will, no doubt, be aware that a knot is one nautical mile per hour) is a universal geographical distance and is readily applicable to maps and charts. One final word on the A.S.I. It is important to remember that the speed indicated is the speed of the aircraft THROUGH THE AIR and not the speed over the ground.

The sensitive altimeter is really an aneroid barometer, but instead of indicating barometric pressure the dial is graduated in height. This conversion is quite simple, as you know that the higher you go the less is the pressure of air pushing down on you. The reduction of air pressure through height is constant and known, but variations of barometric pressure have to be allowed for. The sensitive altimeter has three pointers, and is read rather like a clock. The longest pointer indicates 100s of feet (and the divisions of 20 feet); the next longest 1,000s of feet; and the tiny pointer 10,000s of feet. The adjustment for variations of barometric pressure is made by means of the knob at the bottom of the instrument, and is shown on the scale on the right-hand side of the dial. This scale is graduated in millibars, which is the universal unit of barometric pressure, and although the adjustment of the altimeter is not so very essential in your basic training, you can imagine that it is vital later on, when you will be faced with landing at night or in thick weather, when as pilot you must know your actual height above the ground.

The artificial horizon is the instrument in the top centre of the panel, and is gyroscopically driven. It is primarily an instrument for use in conditions when the natural horizon is obscured to the pilot, *i.e.*, at night or in bad visibility, but later on you will be able to get a lot of useful information from it, as indicating the accuracy of your flying. You will notice that the bottom half of the indicator is graduated in 30 degrees from 0 to 90 degrees right and left. Superimposed in the centre of the instrument, and fixed, is a representation of an aeroplane—your aeroplane *being looked at from the stern* (an important point to remember). The horizon bar, which is shown in the diagram lying across the dial in the bottom left-hand quadrant, will, when the aeroplane is in flight,

PRESSURE INSTRUMENTS

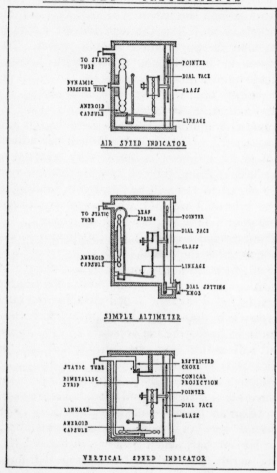

AIR SPEED INDICATOR

SIMPLE ALTIMETER

VERTICAL SPEED INDICATOR

FIG. I.

set itself up across the instrument in a position parallel to the horizon and remain in that relation. In straight and level flight the horizon bar will be parallel to and immediately behind the little aeroplane, in the climbing attitude the horizon bar will be beneath, and in the glide or dive attitude above the little aeroplane. (Think for one moment, and you will see that the instrument gives a representation of the actual positions of the aircraft with relation to the horizon.) The degree of bank in a turn can be read off directly from the graduated scale, but *remember* you are looking at yourself from behind.

Underneath the artificial horizon is the directional gyro, and, as the name implies, this is also gyroscopically driven. It is rather difficult to explain the working of this instrument without going into the whole theory and practice of gyroscopes, which in itself would fill a whole book and would, in any case, be a little beyond our present study. Suffice it to say that it is an easily read compass not subject to the magnetic influence of the earth. After the gyro is set up and has been lined up with the magnetic compass by means of the knob at the bottom of the instrument, a course can be steered by it when in flight.

Next on the panel, at the top right, is the vertical-speed indicator, which indicates rate of climb or descent in feet per minute. The construction of the instrument is somewhat similar to a simple altimeter, as it consists of a capsule inside an air-tight case. The capsule is connected directly to the static pipe of the air-speed indicator. The air-tight case is also connected to the static pipe but through a restricted choke, into which fits a cone. When the aircraft changes height the resulting change in atmospheric pressure is immediately transmitted to the inside of the capsule, but, through the restriction of the choke, the change inside the case is not so rapid. This difference is converted by means of delicate links to give a reading on the dial of hundreds of feet per minute climb or descent.

The turn-and-slip indicator is the instrument in the bottom right-hand corner of the panel, and is of extreme interest in its construction, as the two needles are entirely separate and are even worked by separate means, but they must be read to-gether. The top needle, the slip indicator, is operated by a pendulum which will normally remain in the vertical plane of the aircraft. If some force is applied to the aeroplane (as in a badly executed turn), then that force will either pull or push the pendulum to one side or the other, and the needle will indicate some degree of " slip " or " skid ". (More about these two faults when we get to the chapter on turns.) The turn indicator, the bottom needle, is gyro driven, and works on the principle that a gyro will always resist any motion that tends to deviate it from the plane of rotation, so as the aeroplane turns, the " rate of turn " and direction of the turn will be shown by the pointer. As distinct from the " angle of bank " in a turn, the " rate of turn " is the actual time, in minutes and seconds, taken for the machine to turn through 360 degrees.

The last two instruments are the oil-pressure gauge and the oil-temperature gauge, and I do not think any detailed explanation is required of them, as their names adequately describe their functions, but they are both extremely necessary as guides to the running of the engine.

You will have noticed that when talking of gyroscopic instruments, I have used the term " set up ". As you know the essential part of a gyroscope is a rather heavy wheel rotating at very high revolutions per minute, and you will appreciate that some time must elapse before this rotor is able to run at its maximum speed. During this interval the instrument indications will be inaccurate, but on reaching full speed, when the instrument is " set up ", it will give accurate and continuous readings. There are two methods of driving the rotor, one by an engine-driven pump, the other by means of a Venturi tube.

Our particular type of trainer uses the engine-driven vacuum pump, but I think it would be of interest to you to have the Venturi explained, as, in any case, the object of both methods is to cause a " depression " (a lowering of the atmospheric pressure) inside the air-tight cases of the instruments. On some aeroplanes you may have noticed a peculiar hollow horn. This is the Venturi tube, and it works in the following manner: As the aeroplane moves through the sky air is taken in at the front of the horn and discharged through the back of it, but on its way through, its passage is obstructed by a narrow neck. The action of this narrow neck is to increase the speed of the air, which in turn decreases the pressure at the neck. The cases of the instruments are connected to the area of reduced pressure by means of a pipe-line, so that we now have reduced pressure inside the instrument cases. In each instrument case is fitted a very fine nozzle or jet which admits air at high velocity in an endeavour to overcome the depression inside the case. The jet is directed straight on to the rotor, in the rim of which are a number of little niches which act like the impeller blades in a turbine, gradually the speed of the rotor builds up until it reaches its maximum, and the instrument is then in full working order. In our aeroplane, having the vacuum pump, the instruments begin working much quicker than in machines with a Venturi tube, as the Venturi does not really start work until the machine is air-borne.

Now, to finish with the instrument panel, there are only two more things to mention. First, on the left-hand side you can see the two engine switches. They are down and therefore OFF (remember, the reverse of the electric-light switches in your home). There are two, because the engine has twin magnetos and a double ignition system, partly as a safety precaution and partly to get greater efficiency from the engine. The magneto, being a delicate piece of machinery,

PLATE I

de Havilland " Chipmunk " Trainer.

Percival " Provost " Trainer.

PLATE II

Tail Unit.

Showing the Rudder (vertical control) and the Elevators (horizontal control) and the Fin (to which the rudder is hinged). On the trailing edge of the Elevators can be seen the Elevator Trimming Tabs.

is liable to failure, so if one should fail the other will enable you to get home or to land in safety.

On the right-hand side of the panel you will notice a ring. This is the starter and has to be pulled out to start the engine. The action of pulling the ring fires what is in essence a revolver. The cartridge which is fired looks exactly like the type of cartridge that is fired in shot-guns, but, of course, it does not contain any shot. The blast from the discharge is sufficient to turn the engine over, and providing the switches are on and everything is in order, the engine will start.

Below the panel on the left-hand side of the cockpit are the engine controls. (See Plate III.) One is the throttle which controls the engine speed, and the other the mixture control by which the pilot regulates the richness of the mixture of petrol and air that enters the cylinders. It will be appreciated that the higher the aeroplane climbs the rarer becomes the air, and without this provision the delicate ratio of petrol to air would be upset, thereby affecting the efficient running of the engine. On the outside of the throttle controls you will notice a milled knob which can, and must, be tightened to avoid the throttle vibrating itself closed. It can be slackened off to make for easier working for taxi-ing.

Two other levers in the cockpit need some explanation. The first is the lever which can be seen under the throttle, and which works the brakes, sometimes called the parking brake, but

B

much use can be made of the brakes for taxi-ing,
provided they are used with caution. With the
brake-lever right off (right forward), the application of full rudder will produce some braking
effect on the wheel on the same side as the full
rudder, but the effect can be increased by pulling
the lever back two or three notches. For parking
the aircraft, the lever must be right back, but
if the aircraft is to be parked for any length of
time, it is advisable to put chocks under the
wheels, and let the brake off so that no prolonged
strain is imposed on the brake mechanism and
cables.

The large lever on the right-hand side of the
cockpit operates the flaps. The flaps, as the
name implies, are two flaps which, by means of
the lever, are lowered into the air-stream passing
on the lower side of the wings, and thus alter the
configuration of the wing. The effect is two-
fold. The depression of the flap up to about 10
degrees gives considerable increase in " lift " to
the wing, and is very necessary to get an aeroplane
air-borne quickly, as for instance, taking off from a
small field. Beyond the 10-degree mark, addi-
tional lift will still be gained from the flap, but the
increase of " drag " will be of such proportions
as to cancel this effect. The use of a large
amount of flap will cause the nose of the machine
to be much lower without any great increase in
speed, will permit the angle of descent to be much
steeper, once again without much increase in
speed, as when you are approaching to land, and

will also permit of the aeroplane to be flown safely at slower speeds.

I think that will do now for the description of the cockpit, its instruments and controls, and you must be in need of a " breather " before we go off for our first flight.

CHAPTER II

STARTING-UP AND TAXI-ING

Now that you have recovered your breath after the long but very necessary explanation of the cockpit and the instruments, let us go to our aeroplane, start up, take off, and breathe some fresh air. When you get into your cockpit for your first lesson I will show you how to fix your straps (or safety harness), and how to adjust your helmet and phones ; watch closely what I am doing, so that you can save a lot of time on future occasions. As soon as I am settled in the rear cockpit we will be ready to start, by which time a mechanic will have come up to give us assistance. I always think it safer to consider that, during the operation of starting an aeroplane engine, the mechanic outside is really the person in charge and that the pilot does not take over until the engine is running.

The first thing to do is to report the state of the cockpit to the mechanic outside. This is usually the standard procedure :

" Switches off."
" Petrol on." (The petrol cock is by your left foot.)
" Throttle closed."
" Brakes on."

The mechanic will now prime the engine (this is really the modern way of expressing the old-fashioned habit of " tickling the carburetter "). He will then stand back and indicate to the pilot that all is clear to start. It is now the pilot's responsibility to call " Contact ", at the same time switching on the main engine switches and pulling the starter ring on the right-hand side of the cockpit, thereby firing a cartridge and starting the engine. The throttle setting for starting should be about a quarter of the quadrant forward, so that the revs on starting would be about 500. During starting-up it must be remembered to hold the control column well back, so that the slip-stream passes over the tail and forces it firmly on to the ground.

It is necessary to leave the engine ticking over at this speed in order that the oil may circulate to all the moving parts of the engine, and at the same time to allow the oil temperature to build up. After the oil temperature has reached 30° C., which may take a few minutes, the throttle can be opened until about 1,600 revs are indicated, and each magneto circuit tested separately by switching off one ignition switch at a time. Should a drop of more than 75 revs be indicated on either circuit, it is an indication that the engine requires examination. If this test is satisfactory, open up slowly and firmly to the fully open position, noting the revs on the engine-speed indicator whilst at full throttle. These should be in the region of 2,000 to 2,100, the variation being caused sometimes by the engine and sometimes by the propeller. Then close the throttle until the engine is just ticking over.

In the foregoing I have used the expression " the pilot ", which in actual fact will be you, as from now on it will be your job to start the engine. Having satisfied yourself that the engine and, as far as you can tell, all the instruments appear to be in working order, test all the other controls by means of the control column and rudder bar, and if they seem correct you are now ready to taxi out, but first of all you must wave your hand above your head as an indication to the mechanic to remove the chocks from in front of the wheels.

To taxi an aeroplane may sound a very easy thing to do, and it is, providing care is taken, and above all it is remembered that at no time must you taxi at a speed greater than a good walking-pace. At first you are going to find it a little awkward to handle the machine on the ground, but with care and experience you will come to find that an aeroplane is really quite a handy machine to manage.

You will now move off and taxi out to a position on to the aerodrome from which you will take-off. First of all release the brake to the right off position and gently open the throttle until the aircraft begins to move forward, and then by applying full rudder turn the machine in such a manner as to allow you to taxi to the down-wind side of the aerodrome. You remember that when talking of the brakes I mentioned that the application of full rudder applied brake on the side of the full rudder, and that to make this braking effect more pronounced we move the brake-lever back a couple of notches. Here let me impress on you not to rely entirely on your brakes but as much as possible on the use of the throttle and the rudder, bearing in mind that the greater the slip-stream over the rudder the more effective becomes that control.

As we move forward hold the control column well back into your stomach, so that the slip-stream passing over the elevators will tend to push the tail more firmly on to the ground. This is particularly important when you find it necessary to open the throttle a little wider when turning. You will notice that as you are sitting in the cockpit you have quite a considerable blind spot dead ahead of you, and therefore taxi-ing absolutely straight entails risk of collision. It is necessary therefore, to swing the nose from side to side and if possible to avoid all occasions that necessitate taxi-ing straight ahead. By swinging the nose from side to side I don't mean that your path across the aerodrome should be something like a snake's progress, but by occasionally moving the nose from side to side and keeping a good intelligent look-out we can be assured of safety.

Taxi-ing into wind is relatively easy, but care must be exercised when taxi-ing across wind or down wind, as there is a tendency for the aircraft to have the tail blown round and for the machine to weathercock into wind. Avoid all excessive throttle or brake movements, and if you remember that to taxi slowly is the means of safety, experience will teach you a lot. So to sum up, the important points to remember in taxi-ing are always taxi slowly, always keep a good look-out, use the throttle smoothly and sparingly, and avoid using the brakes harshly.

We have now taxied to a position on the down-wind side of the aerodrome, which will give us the longest possible take-off run into wind, and we will turn the aircraft now to a cross-wind position facing into the circuit (which will be explained in the next chapter), and we will prepare for the take-off.

CHAPTER III

TAKING-OFF

BEFORE I tell you about the take-off it perhaps would be advisable to explain what is meant by a circuit. At all aerodromes there is what is known as a circuit area, which is almost invariably left-hand. This means that aircraft will always fly round the aerodrome by means of doing a series of left-handed turns, and other aircraft coming into the aerodrome will also join in the circuit by mean of left-handed turns. It is remotely possible that you will come across an aerodrome where the circuit is variable—in other words, can be right or left—but the direction of the circuit will always be indicated in the SIGNALS AREA. (See aerodrome signs at the back of the book.)

Now that we have reached the position on the aerodrome which is going to give us our longest possible take-off run, and have turned the nose of the aircraft to the left, we are in the position to do our final check of the cockpit, which should always be systematic and thorough. Such things as checking petrol, oil pressure, maps, safety harness, and to see that the canopy is properly shut, are the sort of things that should be done while sitting across wind.

The reason that the nose is turned in this direction is that on your right will be the direction in which you are eventually going to take-off. Over and round the nose is the circuit, and it is easy for you to see whether there are any other aircraft in the vicinity of the aerodrome; on your left you will be able to see any aircraft that are about to land and to which you have to give way.

Naturally, taking-off is the means whereby we get into the air as quickly and as safely as possible. It is therefore necessary to take-off into wind, because the speed at which the aeroplane is air-borne is dependent on air speed. Suppose, for example, the take-off speed (*i.e.*, the speed at which the machine is air-borne) is 45 knots and there is a 20-knot wind blowing against you, by taking-off into wind the ground speed at the moment of take-off would be only 25 knots, whereas by taking-off down wind the ground speed would be 65 knots. As I have said before, we give ourselves the longest possible run into wind, so that we can gain maximum height before crossing the boundary of the aerodrome, which would enable us to have plenty of time to make an emergency landing in the event of an engine failure, which, happily, is not an everyday occurrence nowadays.

When you are satisfied that everything in the aircraft is in order, take a good look round the whole of the circuit, and if you are not going to get in any one's way, we will turn the machine into wind and take-off with as little delay as possible. For taking-off (Fig. 2) the tail-trim is put to a slightly NOSE-HEAVY position. This is to help you with the control column in getting the tail up as you gather speed. The control column should be held just slightly back of the central position as you open the throttle smoothly to the fully open position. Pick a mark, such as a tree, a building, or a church steeple, as far ahead into

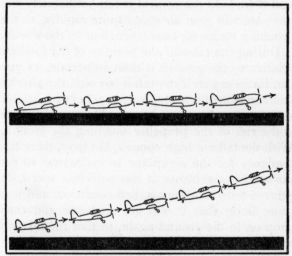

FIG. 2.—Taking-off.

The tail rises and the machine runs along the ground until it has sufficient speed to lift itself into the air and to continue climbing at the correct climbing speed.

wind as is possible, as a mark on which to keep the aeroplane straight. As the effect of full throttle becomes noticeable and the aeroplane is moving across the ground, you must keep it absolutely straight by means of the rudder, at the same time gently easing forward on the control column to get the tail off the ground. The position of the

aeroplane now is that it is rapidly gathering speed
with the wheels still on the ground and the fuselage parallel to it. As the aeroplane begins to
feel buoyant we will ease gently back on the
control column until the wheels leave the ground,
and if we hold the control column absolutely still
now, we will gain air speed quite rapidly, as the
ground is no longer causing friction on the wheels.

During the take-off the position of the fuselage
relative to the ground is most important, as you
can imagine that if the tail is too high the aircraft
will run along for a very long way before it attains
sufficient speed to get air-borne, added to which there
is the risk of the propeller touching the ground.
With the tail not high enough, however, there is a
tendency for the aeroplane to endeavour to get
air-borne long before it has sufficient speed, in
other words, in a semi-stalled condition, and it is
quite likely that it will get air-borne and then
drop on to the ground again, so that the take-off
will look rather like a series of kangaroo hops.

The importance of keeping straight during the
take-off cannot be over-emphasised, and the
quick and accurate corrections by your feet on the
rudder bar are very essential.

CHAPTER IV

FLYING STRAIGHT AND LEVEL

FROM a previous chapter you have learnt the fundamental functions of the controls. Now that we have taken-off and are in the air it is necessary to try the controls and to see the effect. For this reason we will pretend that we have climbed to a safe height and have plenty of room beneath us to recover from any manœuvre.

Take the rudder first. Notice that you have only to put a foot very slightly forward for the nose to start slewing round the horizon. All movements of controls in the air are slight except in aerobatics, and even then they are smooth, gentle, and sure. Ease your right foot forward slightly—now centralise the rudder again. What happened? So long as your foot was forward the nose slewed round to the right slowly, and stopped, pointing in the new direction, as you took off the rudder (centralised the rudder bar). Now do it again and hold it. First the nose starts slewing round to the right along the horizon because the machine is skidding outwards like a car going round an unbanked turn at speed, then the machine begins to bank to the right, and finally the nose begins to drop below the horizon. While this is going on take a quick peep at the turn-and-slip indicator. You will notice

45

that the bottom needle is indicating the direction of the turn, whilst the slip needle is well over to the left.

The machine begins to bank because the outside wing on the turn (the left wing in this case) is travelling faster than the inside wing, and therefore gains more lift, and the nose begins to drop because once the aeroplane is banked it is on a different plane from the horizon, and the rudder, still acting in the same direction relative to the aeroplane, forces the nose down below the horizon.

Now the ailerons. We are flying level again, and you put the stick slightly over to the right. The aeroplane banks to the right (left wing higher than the right wing), the nose at first slews slightly round to the left and up, because of the slight drag caused by the depressed aileron, the aeroplane side-slips to the right because you have not used any rudder to give it a turning movement; and then the nose falls because the lift behind the centre of gravity is greater than in front of it.

Take another quick peep at the turn-and-slip indicator. This time you will notice that the bottom needle remains in the centre or tends to show a slight turn to the right, and the top needle, the slip needle, is still over to the right, indicating that the aeroplane is slipping sideways to the right.

Now the elevator. This is very simple. Ease the stick slightly back and the nose rises above the horizon, slightly forward and it sinks below the horizon. If you keep the stick back too long, the aeroplane will reach a stalled attitude with its nose high in the air, having lost most of its speed. If you hold the stick forward, the aeroplane will dive steeper and steeper and faster and faster until you start easing back on the stick and bring the nose up on to the horizon, when once again it will settle down to level flight.

The position of the throttle for normal cruising is roughly about half-way forward, or about 2,100 revs on the engine-speed indicator.

Before trying to fly straight and level, take a good look round you. Notice that your view is divided into two halves: that which is above the horizon, and that which is below. The horizon stretches right around you. In fact, it is a circle of which you are the centre, and for this reason, any point of it can be used as a guide to fly straight. Whatever your height above the earth, a line joining you to the horizon is a tangent to the curve of the earth. The horizon can therefore be used as a guide to level flight. Similarly, by aligning the wings to the horizon, you can keep the plane flying level laterally.

You will have realised by now that there are three planes in which to fly level—the pitching plane, the rolling plane, and the yawing plane. To fly level laterally you see that one wing is not lower than the other. If it is, ease it up by moving the control column away from it. And to fly level longitudinally, you keep the nose on the horizon by easing the control column backward or forward, as the case may be, and prevent yaw with the rudder. Remember always to hold the control column lightly in the right hand. Never grip it.

A certain amount of practice is required before you can fly level longitudinally, because the mark on the aeroplane which you align with some point on the horizon is different for every aeroplane and for different speeds of the same aeroplane. First let us assume that you are flying along level at cruising speed about 100 knots, that is, with the throttle about half-way forward. Take a look at the altimeter and note your height, and at the airspeed indicator and note your speed. Then fly the aeroplane at what you think is level flight. If the nose is too low, the machine will gain speed and lose height. If you have settled the nose too high, then the machine will lose speed and gain height. By keeping the throttle in the same position, therefore, and by watching the airspeed indicator and the altimeter, you will be able to find the proper attitude of the machine for flying level. Very soon you will be able to determine this position without even glancing at the instruments.

An experienced pilot can fly a new plane for the first time and have no difficulty in finding the level position. He can tell by the change of engine note if he is losing or gaining speed and by the general feel of the aeroplane if he is flying level.

You have realised by now that the faster the air

speed, the harder it is to move the controls, and less movement is necessary to get the required result. There is, therefore, a direct relationship between the feel of the controls and the speed of the aeroplane. This relationship is there without qualification for the ailerons; but the elevator and rudder, being behind the propeller, and therefore in its slip-stream, are affected not only by the speed of the aeroplane but also by the revving of the engine, whether fast or slow. The ailerons are well outside the slip-stream. For this reason it is on the aileron control that a pilot depends so much for the " feel " of his aeroplane.

When the aeroplane is flying near its stalling speed, you will find that the aileron control almost disappears. You can literally waggle the stick from side to side of the cockpit with very little effect. When the aeroplane is flying faster, the aileron control has stiffened up, and it needs quite a lot of push to move the control column from side to side. Here, then, at any time is a perfectly accurate way for the pilot to determine without any reference to instruments how near to his stalling speed—the speed at which the wings lose their lift and as a result the aeroplane sinks towards the earth—he is flying.

CHAPTER V

STALLING, CLIMBING, AND GLIDING

FROM a pilot's point of view the most vital speed of an aeroplane is its stalling speed. This is because it is the speed at which the machine ceases to become air-borne and will sink towards the ground. Any aeroplane may lose considerable height in a stall unless corrective action is taken quickly, and therefore practice stalling must never be done close to the ground, but always at a height that will allow of ample space for recovery.

As it is so vital, it is most necessary for a pilot to be familiar with the symptoms that precede a stall, so that he may avoid it. When you are flying a new aeroplane, therefore, one of the first things to do is to climb to a really safe height and deliberately stall it so that you know just what the symptoms of that particular aeroplane are. The way to do this is simple. When you have gained at least 3,000 feet of height, and are flying straight and level, gently close the throttle so that the engine is just ticking over, and at the same time ease back the control column so that the nose points above the horizon. The machine will quickly lose speed. As it does so, feel your ailerons in the manner described in the previous chapter and notice how they become less and less effective. At the actual point of the stall you will find that you can move the control column the full distance from side to side without having any effect. Another thing that happens as the speed drops is that the nose will appear to become more and more heavy, so that, in order to keep it

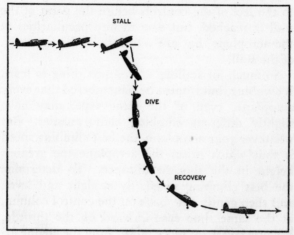

FIG. 3.—Going into and Recovering from a Stall.

above the horizon, you will have to increase the pressure on the control column to keep it back. At the point of the stall the machine appears to hang suspended and motionless in the air. After what seems to be a complete pause in movement, the nose drops, in spite of the fact that your stick is as far back as it can be. In the old days machines used to do funny things when they stalled, but modern machines rarely do anything other than merely drop their nose and perhaps one wing. To recover from a stall, open the throttle fully, at the same time allow the control column to come forward to the centralised position, and the speed will gradually build up and the aircraft will become unstalled. You want to practise a stall several times, not only so that you get used to the feel of the controls before the point of the stall is reached, but also to any peculiarities of the aeroplane that are warnings of the approach of the stall.

So much for stalling. The next thing to learn is climbing, but it must be remembered that every aeroplane, even of the same type, may have slightly different climbing characteristics. But whatever your aeroplane, the best climbing speed is that which raises the aeroplane the greatest height in the shortest distance. To determine the best climbing speed, fly straight and level, and then gently ease back on the control column, at the same time ease forward on the throttle, because you want more power from the engine for climbing. When the nose has risen a little way above the horizon, keep it there and you will notice that the machine loses speed. You will see this by the air-speed indicator, and you will also notice that the speed of the engine appears to be getting slower. As this happens ease the control column from side to side to feel the aileron control. If the ailerons begin to feel ineffective, then you are trying to climb at too steep an angle for maximum efficiency, so ease forward on the control column a trifle and continue to climb with the nose not quite so high above the horizon. You will find that the best climbing speed of your machine, which cruises at about 100 knots, is somewhere in the region of 70 knots, about 800 feet per minute on the vertical-speed indicator.

I hope that from this description it is clear to you that the climbing angle of an aeroplane is the angle between the longitudinal axis of the aeroplane and the horizontal. The best climbing angle is that on which the best rate of climb is maintained. I should perhaps mention that the best climbing angle differs according to your engine power—in other words, according to the position of the throttle; full throttle is important when you are taking-off, as you want to get as high as you can as quickly as you can. When you have reached 1,000 feet or so, and still want to go on climbing, you can ease the throttle back a little and continue to climb at slightly reduced power. This is merely done to take the strain of full throttle off the engine. Although the best climbing angle differs according to the throttle setting, the best climbing speed for all practical purposes remains approximately the same.

Now we come to the gliding, or in modern parlance, descending. This is, in fact, flying with the engine throttled right back so that it is idling at minimum revs. The engine would be " off " only if you cut the switches, but these you do not touch. If the engine fails and cuts of its own accord, then, of course, gliding is flying with the engine off, but this is an involuntary procedure. You have learnt that when climbing you are seeking to gain as much height as possible for horizontal distance covered, and when gliding you seek to lose as little height as possible for horizontal distance covered. This generalisation, like every other one, is liable to modification, but in the main it is true. The pilot throttles back his engine and glides in order to lose height without gaining unnecessary speed. If, owing to trouble, his engine cuts out, he then glides in order to maintain flying speed without use of the engine. He merely calls upon gravity to supply the power to keep him in the air at all, and pays for it by losing height. He has, however, the aircraft under full control all the time.

In many respects gliding is similar to climbing. The gliding angle is the angle between the horizontal axis of the aircraft and the horizontal level, and the pilot maintains his gliding angle by keeping the nose in a set position in relation to the horizon, but instead of the angle of the nose being above the horizontal level or horizon, as in climbing, it is below.

The best gliding speed of an aircraft is determined in a similar way to the best climbing speed, and this is in direct relation to the best gliding angle. In order to start a glide, throttle back as far as the throttle lever will go and ease the nose down a distance below the horizon similar to that it was above it for climbing. The speed of the aircraft will soon decrease, and after the machine has arrived at the correct angle it will settle down to a set speed of round about 60 knots. If the nose is too high, the speed will drop farther, and you will feel your aileron control becoming in-effective again. As soon as this happens, ease the control column forward, and the nose will drop and speed will be regained. If you put the nose too far below the horizon the speed will rise unduly and, as usual, you will be able to detect this by the stiffening of the controls as well as by a glance at your air-speed indicator.

What you must be very careful about in gliding is that you do not glide too slowly. You want to have a good margin of safety above the stalling speed in order to have full control. On rough days you must glide faster than usual in order to be certain of having control under sudden changes of air conditions. The chief use of the glide is for approaching down on to an aerodrome pre-paratory to landing. On the other hand, it is at its greatest value when an engine cut necessitates a pilot making a forced landing without the advan-tage of being able to call on engine power. The gliding that we have considered so far has been without the use of the flaps. We will now lower the flaps to their full limit, and you will notice that as the flaps are depressed into the slip-stream there is a tendency for the nose to be pulled even lower, but without a very great increase in air speed. It will be seen, therefore, that the use of the flaps will enable you to glide at a much steeper angle without any undue increase in air speed.

Gliding is among the most pleasant sensations of flying. Away from the roar of the engine it is a delight to glide smoothly down invisible paths in the air, and especially is it a delight to choose a day when there are fat, billowy, isolated clouds, and to glide in the valleys that they form, being particularly careful to watch for other aeroplanes at all times. But if you glide for more than 1,000 feet at a time, give the engine a burst of throttle every now and again so as to keep it warm.

During the time that you are practising climbing and gliding, have an occasional look at the artificial horizon and see how the representation of your little aeroplane (which, remember, is your own aeroplane looked at from behind) appears to move above or below the horizon bar according to the degree of climb or glide. Remember also that the elevator trim can, and should, be used with advantage during climbing and gliding, so that you are not called on to exert undue pressure on the control column. The exact position for the trim can be determined by the pilot only by means of trial and error until he finds that the control is comfortable.

CHAPTER VI

TURNING

IN order to appreciate the problems involved in the matter of turning an aeroplane, think for a moment of a motor-car. If you take a bend in a flat, level road too fast, there is a tendency for the car to skid outwards and overturn. Arterial roads overcome this tendency by having banked turns, the road being level on the inside and becoming steeper and steeper as the outside of the turn is reached. A car taking the turn slowly keeps on the inside, but one which is going fast takes the corner high up the banking—just how high up depending on its speed and the gradient of the track. Alternatively, the driver may choose his position on the banking and then adjust his speed accordingly. If his speed is adjusted to the banking correctly, he can take the corner with perfect ease, there being no tendency for his car to skid outwards. Supposing he takes the banking too high for the speed he is travelling, then there will be a tendency for his car to slip in or down the slope.

Exactly the same thing happens with an aeroplane, but instead of the pilot flying along a track which is banked, he himself, by means of his aileron control, banks his aeroplane according to his rate of turn. If he banks too much for his rate of turn, the aeroplane will slip inwards; but if he does not bank enough, then his aeroplane will skid outwards. Alternatively, suppose he puts his aeroplane into a set degree of bank and turns too slowly, it will slip inwards; and if he turns too fast, it will skid outwards. Both these mistakes are very easily recognised by a pilot. If his machine is slipping inwards on a left-hand turn, for example, he feels that he is falling inwards, and if it is skidding outwards, he feels a distinct tendency for him to be thrown against the right side of the cockpit. The degree of the slip or skid will be shown on the turn-and-slip indicator.

The effect of the controls on a banked aeroplane is a little confusing at first. The golden rule is to remember that, RELATIVE TO THE AEROPLANE, they work the same. When you ease the control column back, whatever the position of the aeroplane relative to the horizon, the nose always rises in a sort of endeavour to catch its tail; when you put on left rudder (left foot forward) the nose will always yaw towards the left wing-tip, and when you put on right rudder it will always try to yaw towards the right wing-tip. If you bear that in mind, you will have no difficulty in understanding the control movements for going into, holding, and coming out of turns (Fig. 4).

Before trying a turn, think purely theoretically of the function of the elevator and rudder under the two extremes of bank—full bank (90 degrees to the horizon) and no bank (wings parallel to the horizon). You know what happens in the latter

case. Ease the control column back and up goes
the nose, put on rudder and the nose slews round
the horizon towards the inside wing-tip. Now,
then, let us assume that the aeroplane is theoretically suspended in the sky, flying along with full
bank on—that is, with its wings at 90 degrees to
the horizon. What happens when you ease the
control column back? The nose still tries to reach
over your head and catch its tail; but because
the wings are at right angles to the horizon, THE
NOSE SLEWS ROUND THE HORIZON. In other words,

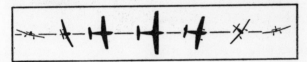

FIG. 4.—Into and out of a Turn.

the elevator has the same effect on the nose
relative to the horizon as the rudder has when the
aeroplane is flying level (Fig. 5).

When you put rudder on in this fully banked
position, the nose still tries to turn towards the
wing-tip, but because the wing is at right angles to
the horizon, the nose actually moves directly
above or below the horizon, according to whether
you put on TOP RUDDER (right foot forward in a
left bank, left foot forward in a right bank) or
BOTTOM RUDDER (right foot forward in a right bank
or left foot forward in a left bank). Intermediate
angles of bank within these two limits call for
compromise between elevator and rudder.

A good rule when turning is always to settle on

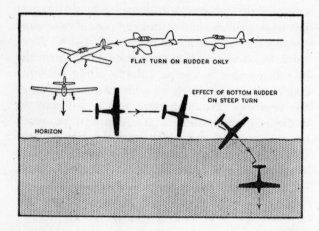

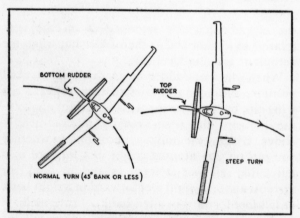

FIG. 5.—When the Machine is Banked, Rudder and Elevator
Tend to Exchange Functions.

This effect increases progressively until the rudder acts as an
elevator and the elevator as a rudder.

an angle of bank and adjust your rate of turn to
that angle, rather than settle on a rate of turn and
adjust your angle of bank to that.

Bearing that in mind, let us try a gentle turn to
the left. Ease the control column over to the left
a little way. This immediately puts on a little
left bank. At the same time put on a little left
rudder to prevent the machine slipping. Because
the machine has left bank on it, the nose will
tend to drop, and the left rudder will also tend to
drop the nose a little below the horizon, as well as
turn it because the machine is on a tilted plane.
You therefore counteract this by easing back on
the control column a little, which has the effect
of lifting the nose up on to the horizon again, but
it also has the effect of helping to turn the
machine. As the bank increases, so the rudder
loses its turning effect and assumes the role of
elevator, and so the elevator loses its " elevating "
effect and assumes the role of steering-control.
But on this first turn we do not wish to do a steep
bank or anything like it. When you have got
10 degrees of bank on, adjust the control column
so that the bank does not get any steeper. I say
" adjust the control column " advisedly, because
you might think that this end is achieved by
centralising the control. In actual fact you will
have to keep the control column a little over to the
right, in order to prevent the bank increasing.
This is because the right wing (the outside wing of
the turn) is travelling faster than the inside wing,
and therefore gaining more lift. Consequently,

if you were to centralise the control column in a
turn, the bank would get steeper and steeper.
You therefore always have to move it a little over
the central position, in order to HOLD OFF the bank.

You must keep the nose just above the horizon
in the same way as when flying level. If you let it
drop too low, the machine will gain speed and lose
height. You pull it up again by adjustment of the
elevator and rudder in the manner described
above. If it gets too high, the machine will lose
speed, and you must bring it down again to the
mean position on the horizon.

You can maintain the correct rate of turn by
your sense of balance. If you are turning too
slowly for the amount of bank you have on, you
will feel the machine slipping inwards, and if your
rate of turn is too fast for the bank, you will feel
the machine skidding outwards. Always remember that it is better to have too MUCH bank
rather than too LITTLE.

When you want to come out of the turn, apply
opposite bank and rudder together. You will
find that more pressure is required on the controls
when coming out of than when going into a turn.
As you take off the bank, so you must adjust your
rudder in order to be properly balanced all the
while; otherwise the machine will skid or slip
coming out of the turn in just the same way as it
will when in the turn, and the rate is not adjusted
to the bank. Care must be taken to keep the nose
in the same position on the horizon as before.
This is again done by a combination of elevator

and rudder; the more the bank is taken off, the less the turning effect to the elevator and the more the rudder, until, when the machine is level again and there is no bank, the elevator and rudder assume once more the normal functions in level flight.

Now try a steep turn. By steep turn I mean anything over 50 degrees of bank. Until you are used to it, you will imagine that you are doing a 90-degree banked turn, when in reality you are doing one much less steep, because the unusual attitude of the machine on its side is misleading.

To make it easier to understand, assume that you are doing a turn with 90 degrees of bank. In actual fact you would not attempt this until you were well practised in less-steep turns. But when your machine has 90 degrees of bank on, you can follow that the rudder becomes the elevator completely and the elevator becomes the rudder. In other words, the only way to adjust the position of the nose on the horizon is by altering the rudder, and the only way to adjust your rate of turn is by means of the elevator. When in this position you can easily understand the meaning of the terms top and bottom rudder, which are used when referring to rudder movements in a turn.

Obviously, when the machine is banked at 90 degrees, it is in position for maximum rate of turn (Fig. 6). This is obtained by holding the control column well back, and quite a lot of force is required to do this. If it is not held back far enough, the rate of turn will be too slow, and the machine will slip violently inwards.

What is most important to remember is that the stalling speed of an aeroplane increases with the amount of bank used in a turn. The stalling speed of an aeroplane flying level may be 50

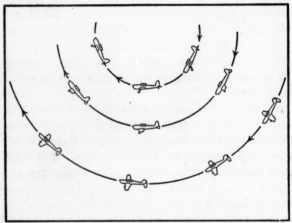

Fig. 6.—Different Rates of Turn showing Attitude of the Machine and Path followed viewed from above.

knots, but when it is in a 90-degree banked turn it is probably about 85 knots. For this reason, when you do a steep turn, ALWAYS USE MORE THROTTLE, and if you are going to hold it for a complete turn, have the throttle as far open as it will go.

When practising turns, do not get into the habit of always turning in the same direction. You will find, if you are right-handed, it is easier to do

PLATE III

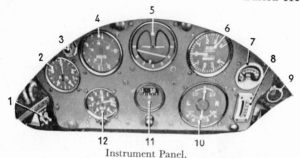

Instrument Panel.

1. Ignition switches. 2. Tachometer or rev counter. 3. Generator warning light. 4. Air-speed indicator. 5. Artificial horizon. 6. Vertical-speed indicator. 7. Oil-temperature gauge. 8. Oil-pressure gauge. 9. Starter. 10. Turn-and-slip indicator. 11. Directional gyro. 12. Altimeter.

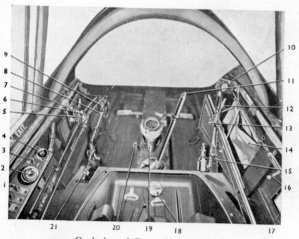

Cockpit and Controls Layout.

1. Lighting switches. 2. Cockpit lamps OFF and DIMMER switches. 3. Identification light switch. 4. Identification light morsing push-button. 5. Throttle and mixture controls friction nut. 6. Mixture control. 7. Throttle control. 8. Brakes control. 9. Master electrical switch. 10. V.H.F. radio controller. 11. Press-to-transmit push-button. 12. Flaps control. 13. Amber screens (used only for blind flying). 14. Goggles stowage. 15. Hand fire extinguisher. 16. Air-intake heat control. 17. Compass-deviation card holder. 18. Harness release box. 19. Magnetic compass. 20. Fuel-cock control. 21. Elevator trimmer wheel.

PLATE IV

Old Type Pitot Head with the Static (upper) and Pressure
(lower) Tubes Separate.

New Type Pitot Head with the Two Tubes Combined.
This type can be electrically heated to prevent icing.

turns to the left, and to do them to the right requires much more concentration. If you are going to favour one turn above the other, favour the right-hand turn. If you get proficient in that you will automatically be proficient in the other.

Another important thing to remember is : never assume that you have the sky to yourself. Before you make a turn, always look around in the direction you are going to turn to see that there are no other aircraft near. One is very much inclined to think that the sky is so large that the risk of collision is infinitesimal, but collisions do happen, and are very much worth guarding against!

Coming out of a steep turn requires a lot of practice before you can do it smoothly with correct synchronisation of controls to avoid slipping or skidding, but if you concentrate hard, you will not find it too difficult. However, never be satisfied unless you come out quite cleanly, with the nose steady on the horizon all the time and rudder and elevator doing their job with precision.

Climbing and gliding turns are almost the same as level-flight turns, the only difference being in the attitude of the machine relative to the horizon. But because the stalling speed in a turn is higher than when the machine has no bank on, great care must be taken that you are either climbing or gliding with ample speed. A climbing turn must be made with more speed than you use when just climbing, and you cannot normally do steep climbing turns because of the rapid loss of speed.

c

A golden rule is never to do climbing turns near the ground.

The same thing applies to gliding turns. Better far to have too much speed than too little. Because the engine is throttled back in a glide, the elevator and rudder will not be so sensitive, so that coarser movements will be required to get the desired result. This need not bother you. Just move the controls firmly but gently always sufficiently far to obtain the desired result. Before going into a gliding turn, lower the nose slightly to get the little extra desired speed for a safe turn, and then ease it up again when you have completed the turn.

And always feel your ailerons in all these manœuvres, so that you can be automatically sure that you are not near stalling speed.

CHAPTER VII

SPINNING

ONE of the most spectacular evolutions is the spin, but although it is one of the most spectacular evolutions, it is, curiously enough, an important feature of a pupil's training long before he starts learning aerobatics. This is because an aeroplane may automatically fall into a spin if the pilot manipulates his controls wrongly when near the point of stall. Generally speaking, an aeroplane will spin if it stalls at any moment when one or more of the controls are in an extreme position. Some aeroplanes are more vicious in this respect than others, and one is relieved to find that more and more types of aeroplanes are now being built that are positively reluctant to go into a spin even when the pilot endeavours to spin. But a pupil must learn to spin in order to be familiar with it at any time, and in order that he may get out of it with a minimum loss of height.

The simplest way to put a machine into a spin is to shut off the engine and ease the nose well up until, at the point of stall, the control column is right back. When this moment is reached, put rudder hard on in whichever direction you wish to spin. The machine will appear to hang still in the air, then its wing-tip will drop, the nose will fall suddenly, and the whole will revolve round and round a vertical axis. Until one is used to it, the sensation of spinning is awe-inspiring. You see the earth revolving very fast around the nose, the machine making a swish-swish-swish sound. A curious feature about it is that when you first do spins, although you may have done only three complete turns, you will feel that you have done twenty-three.

In order to resume normal flight you check a spin in two stages. First you stop the spinning, and then you come out of the resultant dive. The first stage you achieve by putting on full opposite rudder, then easing the control column forward. After about a turn the machine will stop spinning, and you will find yourself in a steep dive. You come out of this by centralising the rudder and gently easing the control column back until normal flight is resumed.

I have already said that, generally speaking, an aeroplane will spin if it is allowed to stall when one or more of the controls are in an extreme position. Let us consider when this is likely to happen.

Suppose you are gliding down in a fairly steep turn. If you are flying near the stalling speed (remember the stalling speed in a turn is higher than when flying level, and this is sometimes forgotten), and you put on too much bottom rudder, the nose will drop and the machine will skid outwards. In a fit of mental aberration you might quite well forget the attitude of the plane, and pull the stick back in an endeavour to get the nose up again. If you do this, the controls are all set for a spin.

STALLING WING DROPPING

IN SPIN

RECOVERY

DIVING OUT

FIG. 7.—Into and out of a Spin.

Suppose you are doing a normal turn with engine on but with none too much speed to spare and you put on too much bottom rudder. The machine will skid outwards, the nose will drop, and you may endeavour to get it up again by pulling back on the stick. Here again, if you do this, the controls are all set for a spin.

Suppose you are doing a steep turn with none too much speed to spare, and you put on too much TOP rudder. The stick is already well back (the ideal position for a spin), and you may find the machine falling into a spin in the opposite direction to the turn.

If you side-slip steeply with the stick too far back and at a speed near the stall, the machine may fall into a spin in the opposite direction to the side-slip.

You must not think, as a result of reading this chapter, that an aeroplane takes every opportunity to spin. It does not; but the spin is always waiting to teach the slovenly airman a lesson. Fly accurately, and you will never get into an unintentional spin. Even fly badly, and you will not get into a spin. But fly very badly, and the spin will be with you at once. Fly accurately and carefully, and you will be quite all right. Even be sure never to have too much rudder on, and you will be all right. But do a lot of practice spinning so as to be prepared for an emergency. I have given spinning a chapter to itself, because it is important.

CHAPTER VIII

APPROACHING AND LANDING

Now you come to the most difficult part of your course of flying instruction—approaching and landing. It is difficult because it cannot be done without perfect judgment, and judgment comes only with experience. So often a pupil does everything very well in the air, but when he comes to learn how to land, nothing seems to go right, and he gets discouraged. I always found that it took more time to teach a pupil how to land (up to the stage when he could go solo) than it took for him to learn everything else— turning, gliding, climbing, taking-off, spinning, etc. You require great patience and a will of iron, and then everything will be all right. But do not expect to learn how to approach and land as easily as you have learnt everything else.

As I have stated before, in this book I am teaching you the various evolutions in the proper sequence of flight. In other words, together we have gone through the procedure of how to fly an aeroplane from the time you get into it outside the hangar to the time you land it. In practice you will not learn in that sequence, because some evolutions are more difficult than those that follow them, and therefore you are taught the later

—simpler—ones first. But in a book of instruction there is no necessity for one to switch about. It merely makes it confusing, and not so interesting. However, we have now come to the stage when our instruction conforms to the sequence of practical instruction. From now on we travel a course parallel to that which you will be given when you are really learning to fly.

When you have come to the end of a flight and it is time to land, take a look over the side at the aerodrome. It looks mighty small, doesn't it? No wonder, then, that much practice is required in judging your glide so that your wheels touch down just where you want them to. At first you can but be content with alighting on the aerodrome, but later on you MUST not be content with anything else but landing within a few yards of a previously selected point. If you always try to do this, you may be sure that on the rare occasion when the need arises you will have the maximum chance of pulling off a successful forced landing in a field of limited space. Besides, it is a grand game to play, compared to which any other is child's play. The satisfaction of gently alighting an aeroplane on a predetermined spot must be experienced to be believed.

Just where one lands is dependent on judgment of the approach. An aeroplane always lands at the same speed, which is the speed at which it stalls. The approach has therefore to be made so that this stalling speed is reached immediately above the point at which you want to alight.

And when I say "above", I do not mean hundreds of feet above. I mean 6 INCHES above. You have already learnt what an aeroplane does when it stalls in the air. It does exactly the same when you land it; but as it is only a few inches above the ground, it sinks those few inches, and its weight is taken by the ground-surface. If you misjudge your landing, and instead of there being only a few inches between wheels and ground at the moment of stall there are a few feet, the machine will drop heavily on to the ground.

The approach is always made into wind. The first thing to do, therefore, is to find out the direction of the wind. This is easily done by looking at the wind-sock on the aerodrome, but during a flight you should always bear in mind the direction of the wind, so that you are prepared for any sudden landing.

Smoke-stacks are the most satisfactory means for checking up on wind direction.

The normal approach is started at about 1,000 feet. This means that you place the machine in a favourable position to alight on the aerodrome from 1,000 feet with engine throttled back and the machine in a glide. You can appreciate that the machine will cover more ground while losing 1,000 feet of height by gliding into a 5-mile-an-hour wind than it will by gliding with a 20-mile-an-hour wind against it. Every approach is therefore different, and adjustment of position has to be made according to the strength of wind. If you start your approach at right angles to the wind

and glide down a path parallel to the boundary of
the aerodrome but about 400 yards behind it, you
give yourself a margin for error (Fig. 8).   At any
time during the glide down that path you can
turn into wind and still land on the aerodrome.
If you are too high to start with, you continue to

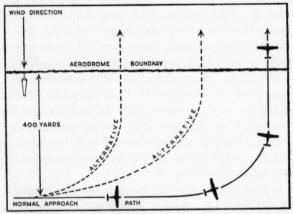

FIG. 8.—Give yourself a Margin of Error by gliding down a Path
   about 400 yards outside and parallel to the Aerodrome
   Boundary at Right Angles to the Wind.

glide down, losing height until you are sure you
can get into the aerodrome; but if you are
comparatively low to start with, you turn into
wind immediately you come abreast of the aerodrome.   Between these two limits is allowance for
a healthy margin of error.

In the approach the great thing to avoid is
UNDER-SHOOTING (finding yourself at the last
moment without enough height to get into the

aerodrome without a burst of engine). This is a
very common fault with beginners. The remedy
is to turn in to the aerodrome when you estimate
that you will touch down near the far hedge, but
you can be pretty sure that you will have touched
down long before this, because of the tendency to
under-shoot. Later on, when you have become
practised in this difficult art, the point on the
aerodrome to aim for is about one-third the way
across it. You can always lose height by side-
slipping (you will learn this later on), but you
can never regain height without engine. In a
forced landing you have no engine, so that it is
essential for you to become accustomed to judge
every approach you make on to an aerodrome
without calling on the engine to get you out of a
difficulty.

Presumably the urge to avoid using the engine
when under-shooting is due to the fact that it is an
acknowledgment of failure to judge the approach
properly, and also to the leg-pulling of your fellow
pupils. Pay no attention to those who scoff at
you. The experienced pilot will commend you for
having the sense to acknowledge a mistake and to
use your engine to get out of its consequences.
But you must not make a habit of it.

During your approach always keep a sharp look-
out for other aircraft, because the vicinity of an
aerodrome is always where you find most aircraft.
Glide down at a good speed—about 60 knots—
and as soon as you have shut off your engine to
begin the glide, lower the flaps the required

amount and ease back the tail-trim so that the control column is light in your hand.

Now we come to landing. We assume that you have judged your approach correctly, so that when you are about 400 feet up you have turned into wind and are coming down in a nice, steady, straight glide, which will result in the aircraft touching down in the centre of the aerodrome. If you find that you have misjudged the approach in such a way that a last-minute turn close to the ground is necessary, then put your engine full on, fly across the aerodrome, gaining height again, and make another circuit. Indeed, whenever you are in the slightest doubt about your judgment, play for safety and do another circuit. You can go on doing this quite happily until your petrol gives out, which will probably be a long time ahead. Incidentally, always keep an eye on your petrol-gauge so that you are not caught napping with an empty tank. The gauge is on the wing, easily visible from the cockpit.

The essence of landing is to glide down at an angle to the ground, and then, when within a few feet of the surface, to alter the attitude of the aircraft to flight along a path 6 inches to 1 foot above the ground and parallel to it (Fig. 9). The machine must proceed along this path until it loses speed to such an extent that its stalling speed is reached and it will sink the 6 inches to make a perfect landing. That is the essence of landing.

I have deliberately omitted aerodynamical explanations in this book, as the student who

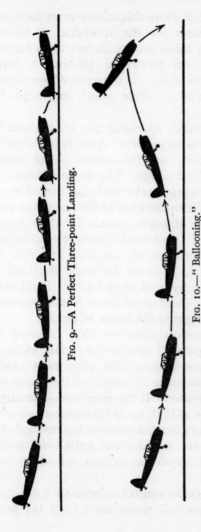

Fig. 9.—A Perfect Three-point Landing.

Fig. 10.—"Ballooning,"

Machine has touched down on its wheels before losing flying speed, and has bounced into the air at an angle which will probably produce a stall.

wishes to delve into this science must do so in text-
books written for the specialist. I have only
referred to aerodynamic factors in so far as they
are part and parcel of piloting a machine.
But we now come to a phenomenon regarding
an aeroplane in flight which must be briefly
explained.

Very broadly speaking, the lift derived by an
aeroplane is dependent upon two things. The
first is speed, and the second is the ANGLE OF
ATTACK of the wings. The angle of attack is the
angle the wings make with the direction of air-
stream. When the nose of the aeroplane is raised
this angle of attack is increased; when depressed,
the angle is decreased. Now we come to the
point with regard to landing. In order to fly
level at, say, 75 knots the angle of attack is less
than it is to fly level at 50 knots. The loss of lift
due to the slower speed has to be compensated for
by the increase in the angle of attack.

It is therefore apparent that, in order to fly
along the parallel path to the surface of the aerodrome when landing, the pilot must gradually
increase the angle of attack of the wings as the
speed decreases. If he does this correctly, the
nose will be as high up as his elevator can get it at
the moment when his machine has reached stalling
point, and the machine will settle comfortably on
the ground, his stick as far back as it will go into his
stomach.

If he eases the control column back too quickly,
the machine will climb away from the ground;

if he does not do it quickly enough, the wheels will touch down prematurely, with the tail still in the air. For an absolutely correct landing, wheels and tail-wheel touch the ground simultaneously in a THREE-POINT LANDING.

If the pilot fails to ease the control column back quickly enough and the wheels touch before the machine has lost flying speed, the machine will in all probability BALLOON into the air (Fig. 10). On touching the ground, the wheels will bounce, thus immediately and suddenly increasing the angle of attack of the wings by bouncing the nose into the air. Because the machine still has flying speed, this sudden increase will cause it to do a sudden climb, resulting quite possibly in a stall 10 feet or so above the ground. Whatever happens, a pilot must not try to force his machine to settle on the ground. It will not do so until it has lost flying speed, and any sudden movement of the control column back will result in the machine ballooning. Thus it can be seen that there is only one way to do a landing, and that is to judge it properly.

The steady approach down on to the aerodrome that I have advocated is necessary so that you can have plenty of time to see that you are landing dead into wind. The wind-sock on the aerodrome will tell you only the approximate direction. When you notice that you are drifting to one side or the other final adjustment has to be made as you glide down. If you see that you are drifting to the left—that is, the machine is moving bodily sideways to the left—you cannot be pointing directly into wind. Put on a little right bank and rudder, so that the nose points into the wind. You can tell how far to turn by looking at the ground and steering straight as soon as you see that you have no drift.

You will probably find that it is best to look out of the cockpit to the left and ahead. It is more comfortable than looking out to the right. However, you must not forget occasionally to cast your eyes out of the right side of the cockpit to see that the way is clear as you approach.

Fix your eyes on a point at an angle of about 45 degrees to the aeroplane and about 40 feet ahead. If you look at the ground too close to you the surface is a blur, and it is consequently difficult to judge your landing.

Having changed your glide down into flight parallel to the surface of the aerodrome, HOLD OFF the machine by gradually easing back on the control column until it gently stalls on to the ground. You can appreciate that, as you are flying to such fine limits above the ground when landing, there is no scope whatever for mistakes, and it is for this reason that landing takes so long to learn. You can turn inaccurately and get away with it, but you can never land inaccurately without damage to the machine.

If you glide down too fast, you will use up a lot of the aerodrome before the machine loses speed sufficiently to stall. Take care, then, to keep your glide down to the correct speed, and do not forget

to feel your ailerons, so that you are independent
of instruments to tell you your speed.

When you are learning and practising after you
have gone solo, there will be many occasions
when you fail to judge the landing properly.
Either you will not hold off long enough, and the
wheels will touch down too soon, perhaps causing
the machine to balloon, or you will hold off too
long and too high, and you will find yourself
suspended ominously near the stall feet above the
ground instead of inches.   On any such occasion
open the throttle fully and go round again.   But
do not try climbing straight away.   Fly level
above the ground until the machine has gathered
sufficient speed for climbing, BUT DO NOT RAISE
YOUR FLAPS UNTIL YOU HAVE ABOUT 400 FEET OF
HEIGHT.   This is most important.   The reason is
because the action of raising your flaps results in a
certain loss of height, so that if you do it too low
your aircraft will sink on to the ground.

If you find that you are going to OVER-SHOOT,
then it is possible to get rid of your surplus height
by SIDE-SLIPPING (Fig. 11).   Side-slipping is merely
a way to steepen the descent WITHOUT INCREASING
THE SPEED.   The way to side-slip from a straight
glide is to first of all yaw the nose out of wind
and at the same time apply OPPOSITE bank and
hold sufficient rudder on to prevent the machine
from turning.   By side-slipping in this manner you
will be automatically correcting any drift and at
the same time slipping down your line of approach.   To recover from the side-slip you must

yaw the nose back into wind and at the same time level the wings with the control column.

A refinement of side-slipping is when it is done while on a turn. Frequently it is convenient to slip off height whilst turning in to the aerodrome. All that the pilot has to do is to put on more bank

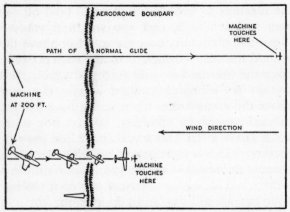

Fig. 11.—Comparison between Normal Glide Path and a Glide shortened by Side-slipping, thus making Possible a Longer Landing Run.

than is actually necessary for his actual rate of turn, and the machine will slip in. To do this he must keep plenty of speed, and not do it too close to the ground, as the loss of height is very rapid.

In rough-weather conditions gliding in to land must be done at a faster speed. Instead of gliding in at 6o knots, it is better to be at 65 knots. This is so that you will have plenty of control when encountering sudden lulls near the ground or rough forces on either wing that necessitate plenty of control to combat them.

If, after landing, you find that the wind is so strong that you are unable to steer the machine on the ground, wait on the aerodrome until some-one comes to lend a guiding hand on a wing-tip. On rare occasions conditions may be so bad that a pilot has to judge his landing to touch down exactly where men are waiting to catch hold of his aircraft. Any wind above the stalling speed of the aircraft will tend to make it fly when it is standing still on the ground. There is therefore good reason for requiring assistance on the ground.

Let me repeat, for safety's sake, whenever you are carrying out a landing do not blind yourself to everything else that may be happening. Remember that the air around an aerodrome has more aeroplanes in it than anywhere else, so always keep a very good look-out for other machines. For this reason do not get into the habit of always looking over the same side of the cockpit when you are approaching. Take frequent glances all around you. And remember, too, that there may be obstacles on the ground that do not show up well from the air, so never assume that the landing area is clear for you. If you have any doubt at all as to whether the stretch of ground you have chosen to land on is not entirely clear and suitable (it may, for instance, be boggy), fly over it first, and then approach and land. AND ALWAYS HAVE PLENTY OF SPEED.

POWERED APPROACH

Modern aircraft characteristics necessitate a technique of approach that includes the use of engine.

You have seen the effect of flaps on the glide during the approach on to the aerodrome. They enable a steeper approach to be made without an increase in speed, and in consequence are an aid to judgment.

Your judgment can be made still easier by a judicious use of engine. Instead of throttling right back when starting the approach with flaps down, throttle back to a point where the engine is doing about 800 revs. This will have the effect of flattening the glide.

Aim at doing precisely the same as though you were making an engine-off approach, that is, get into a position that will bring you on to the aerodrome at constant gliding speed (as without engine) without gaining or losing speed, and then, after flattening out, ease back the throttle, when the aircraft will sink on to the ground as before.

The way to effect your approach under these conditions is to keep the speed constant by raising or lowering the nose as necessary, and by regulating your rate of descent by throttle movements. Thus, if you are under-shooting, ease the throttle open, at the same time easing the nose up to avoid increasing speed. If you are over-shooting, ease back the throttle a little, at the same time lowering the nose to maintain constant speed.

CHAPTER IX

CROSS-COUNTRY FLYING

THE exquisite joy of your first cross-country flight on your own can only compare with your first solo for ripe satisfaction. There is something that defies description about leaving the earth at one spot and coming down an hour later at another in a totally different environment without the gradual adjustment to one's senses that one experiences in a car. The most hard-boiled of men cannot fail to get a lilt when he feels his wheels touch for the first time on " foreign " soil. But just in the same way as you can be a good or a bad aerobatic pilot, so you can be a good or a bad cross-country pilot. Only industry and application will make you good. But the trouble is that the delights of flying are such, some of the fruits are so easy to taste, that one is inclined to take the easy way and avoid the parts that need those qualities—industry and application. Only in recognition and acknowledgment of them, tempered with earnest concentration, does there lie efficiency and—as far as flying is concerned—SAFETY.

The two most important adjuncts to cross-country flying are a compass and a map. The two you use in conjunction. Without a map the compass loses 90 per cent of its value, and without a compass a map loses about 40 per cent of its value. Let us fly from A to B and see what has to be done in order to be sure of finding the way.

First you draw a line connecting A to B on your map. You measure off from this line the distance and the course. The distance, let us say, is 100 nautical miles, and the course due North. Now we have already reached a snag. Although the course measured on the map is due North, we have to make an adjustment, because the magnetic compass points to what is known as the Magnetic North, which alters a little every year, but just now is about 9 degrees West of True North. This is known as VARIATION. The course to set on the compass is therefore 9 degrees to the East of North. Examine the features marked on the map over which your line is drawn. See what are the main landmarks. There will be a town here and a clearly defined wood there; or the railway line crosses your course twice, and a big river sprawls across too. Note just how far these various landmarks are from your starting point, and convert the distance into the time it will take you to reach them.

If, for instance, there is no wind and the first big landmark is a town 20 nautical miles away, at a cruising speed of 100 knots over the ground you will reach this town in twelve minutes. On a perfectly clear day this calculation may not be necessary, but on a foggy day it is a great help to know, by the time taken, just how far along your course you are, so that you may be prepared to look out for landmarks. If the visibility is only a mile, and you are travelling at nearly 2 miles a minute, there is none too much time to check your position by fitting to the pattern of the map the mental picture you have made of some combination of features beneath you. Knowledge of the distance you have travelled, gained by calculating it from time taken and speed of machine, is also of inestimable value when you are expecting to come across a landmark (perhaps it is a railway line crossing your course) and you fail to find it. If you do not see it, the only way of knowing your approximate position (and therefore if you have passed it without seeing it) is by your watch.

Almost invariably there is some sort of wind blowing—wind which, at heights, is blowing from a different direction and with a different speed from that on the ground. On a cross-country flight it is therefore necessary to allow for wind direction and speed when you are working out on what course to fly.

After very few cross-country flights you will begin to get an idea of the number of degrees to steer into wind when you are flying a course across wind or its variants. On the day you fly this journey from A to B suppose there is an easterly wind of 20 knots; that means that, in order to allow for it and steer a course over the ground of 9 degrees East of North, you will have to steer a course in the air a little more to the East—about 12 degrees. Set your compass, then, to 021 degrees. After taking off, fly round and over the aerodrome at the height you are going to fly the journey at, and, when over the centre of the aerodrome, settle on your course by compass.

Having settled on the course that you estimate will take you direct from A to B allowing for DRIFT (wind), keep on it until you fly above a landmark marked on your map. If this landmark is shown on the map to have your pencil line through it, well and good. You made your calculation for drift correctly. But if you find that the landmark is to the East of the course you are steering, then make more allowance for wind, add on another 2 degrees to your compass course, and steer 023 degrees instead of 021 degrees. By this method of trial and error you can very soon find the course to steer, and you are independent of everything but your common sense and experience. With a little of the latter in your bag, you will have no difficulty in finding your course within five minutes of leaving the aerodrome.

Once you know the course to steer, the essential thing is to trust your compass. On occasions you will find, especially in bad weather, that when an expected landmark does not turn up, you will think that you are steering too much this way or that, or even that your compass has taken into its head to go wrong. On such occasions keep *your* head and trust your compass. It will not have gone wrong. Calculate from the time taken from the last recognised landmark just how far from it you are, and lay this distance along the line on your map. You will be mighty near that point, although you can gain no clue to your whereabouts from the earth that speeds swiftly by below you. When, by your time calculation you are quite sure you have passed it, it may be a good idea if it is a good mark like a railway line, to turn back on the RECIPROCAL COURSE (reverse course) and look again. Or, if you come across a railway line and you are lost, fly along it until it leads you to a well-defined town or junction that you will be able to recognise from your map, bearing in mind your rough location.

With the introduction of the present-day system of Air Traffic Control, cross-country flying is not the simple exercise that it used to be. As is well imagined, it is very necessary to have all aircraft movements known by a central control point, particularly as the volume of air transport is increasing every day, and it is therefore most undesirable to have small aeroplanes flitting in and out of the air lanes that are being used by air-liners.

Before embarking on our trip from A to B, it is, therefore, necessary to visit the Air Traffic Control Officer at aerodrome A and inform him of our intentions. He will in turn inform us of the course (or courses, as it may not be permitted to fly direct to B) to steer, of the height at which to fly, of alternative aerodromes to use, and information of any areas to be avoided. He will also give us meteorological information such as the wind speed and direction, and barometric pressures (which will be applied to our sensitive altimeter) and what weather we are likely to encounter on the trip.

With this information we now submit a " flight plan " to the Air Traffic Control Officer, who in due course informs the appropriate control centre of our trip, together with the expected departure and arrival times. From this you will see that the control centre is now aware of where we ought to be at any time from our take-off to our arrival at B.

You should not really set off on a cross-country flight before you have become reasonably proficient at forced landings. These you can practise assiduously in the vicinity of your aerodrome. Although forced landings are fortunately rare nowadays, engines do still fail on occasions, and it is as well to be equipped to deal with such sudden emergency. Anyone can soon learn to fly an aeroplane, but much practice and patience are required before you can be competent to deal with emergencies, so do not be satisfied with your flying until you ARE competent to deal with emergencies.

There are two main difficulties about a forced landing. The first is the ability to choose a suitable place in which to land, and the second is the ability to judge your approach accurately without the use of an engine to get you out of a difficulty.

Curiously enough, although you might not think it, the first of these difficulties is the one that gives most trouble. You can practise forced landings at your home aerodrome until you have attained a high standard of judgment, but it is very much harder to gain competence in recognising suitable landing-surfaces from the air. The only way to do this is to do dummy forced landings when you are on a cross-country flight. Approach on to a likely field and open up the engine just before you touch down. After you have done a few of these, the awful truth will be borne upon you that fields are not as flat as they look from the air, nor are they necessarily as smooth as they look. But when you are doing these dummy approaches take care you do not do them anywhere near livestock. Unfortunately, careless pilots have done tremendous damage to livestock by frightening them at critical periods of their lives. Even healthy young horses have been known to be impaled in a mad endeavour to jump an impossible fence in order to flee from the terror in the sky.

The first thing you must do when your engine suddenly stops is to gain as much height as possible before commencing the glide. At the same time look over the side and give a quick glance at all the ground within gliding distance. Then eliminate the areas that are definitely too small for you to land in. In this connection it is a good idea, when you are on your cross-country flights, to get into the habit of choosing fields in which to land supposing your engine failed at any moment. After a time you will do this unconsciously, and at the moment of trial you will not be unprepared.

If there is a suitable one always choose a grass field in which to land, but do not take for granted that it is smooth. If you look closely at it you may see that it has furrows. In which case it may be all right for you if you land along the furrows. This may involve a cross-wind landing, which is quite feasible provided the wind is not to strong or, if it is strong, if the direction of the furrows is not too much across it. When estimating in your mind whether a field is big enough to land in, remember that the final approach is an important factor. If it is bordered by a high fence, houses, or trees, then you will not be able to touch down in the field until some distance from its boundary.

As soon as you have selected your field, have a look round inside the cockpit to see if you can ascertain the cause of the engine failure. You may perhaps have caught the switches when you were unfolding a map, or perhaps the petrol-cock has inadvertently been turned off.

The best procedure for the approach is to glide as soon as possible to the leeward side of the selected field and then lose height by gliding parallel to it, so that you can turn in immediately you are at the correct height to touch down in the field. Do your turns towards the field, and guard against the tendency to get nearer and nearer to it. Judge the approach so that you touch down about a third of the way up the field; you can always side-slip away surplus height at the last moment; but you cannot gain height without your engine. Always, then, have too much height rather than too little. You will not hurt yourself if you run into the far hedge at the end of your landing-run, but you WILL hurt yourself if you hit the leeward hedge when you are going at flying speed.

The great thing to remember is, once you have selected your field, stick to it. Do not change at the last minute. Almost certainly it will look much more unsatisfactory than you supposed when you were higher up, but never mind. Do not confuse your judgment by last-minute changes. For this same reason, when you have made certain that the engine has definitely failed, close the throttle, and keep it closed. Otherwise it may give a temporary burst just as you are about to land and leave you in a really bad position by failing again at no height and with nowhere suitable to land. Keep a very good look-out for telephone-wires and power-cables. These have a nasty habit of remaining invisible.

It is important to learn the characteristics of the chief types of land that are liable to be met with by a pilot faced with a forced landing.

GRASS appears a dull uniform green or, in autumn, a brownish-green colour. It may often be recognised by the presence of horses, cattle, or sheep grazing on it, but beware of dark lush grass : it might mean boggy conditions.

STUBBLE appears buff coloured in the autumn, according to the time which has elapsed since the crop has been cut. In stubble regular rows can generally be seen. Stubble is one of the best surfaces for landing on.

GROWING CROPS.—The colour of these varies

according to the seasons, but is much brighter in spring and lighter in colour than grass or stubble. They can be recognised by their regular appearance and by the spaces generally found between rows. Crops should be avoided, especially in summer. In a strong wind, high crops and long grass show ripples or waves as the wind passes through them.

ROOT CROPS appear dark green from the air and with regular rows. Root crops make a bad landing-ground but may be used as such in an emergency if an aircraft is landed slowly parallel to the rows or furrows of the crop, provided that the velocity and direction of the wind allow.

PLOUGHED LAND is more general in late autumn and winter, and has a rich brown or red colour which varies according to the soil of the district. Ploughed land makes a bad landing-ground except in very dry or frosty weather.

SAND appears very light yellow or almost white when dry, and varies greatly in its suitability as a landing-ground. Dry, shifting sand is generally too soft for landing, but sand that is moist and firm is suitable. On a beach the sand a few yards from the water's edge is generally suitable.

SNOW is very uncertain, and possesses the disadvantage of concealing the surface and of rendering obstacles invisible. The pilot should scan the surface for shadows, which may indicate an obstacle or a depression in the ground, and should endeavour to execute a very slow landing.

WATER.—A normal landing should be made as

near to the shore as practicable. The aircraft should be held off a little higher than normal, so that the alighting is made with as little forward speed as possible and with the tail well down.

In this chapter I have dealt with the most elementary methods of cross-country flying, the simple example of course finding coupled with map reading, but if you would like to study this fascinating subject more thoroughly, I can strongly commend to your attention a sister volume in this series *Teach Yourself Air Navigation*.

CHAPTER X

AEROBATICS

THERE are those who think that aerobatics are nothing more than evolutions to be indulged in by young pilots anxious to show off to their friends below. The fact is, that apart from the obvious application of aerobatics to air fighting by the military pilot, experience of them is a great asset to the ordinary pilot. They are a means of providing him with confidence in himself and his machine. By deliberately putting his machine into an unusual manœuvre and knowing how to come out of it, he is likely to be able to cope with that emergency which may come once in a lifetime when, from some set of circumstance, he finds himself in a frightening attitude in a storm very close to the ground. Familiarity with aerobatics makes a pilot free from the fear that might beset him on such an occasion and capable of safely recovering from the situation. Aerobatics are also bound to give a pilot confidence in his machine. Obviously some machines are not designed for aerobatics, and the fact that the pilot cannot perform them does not mean that he will lack confidence in the aircraft.

The golden rule is, of course, not to do aerobatics low down. Low stunting must only be carried out by pilots engaged at flying meetings to

PLATE V

AERODROME SIGNALS

Signals area.

Consists of a hollow square about 40′ × 40′ situated near to the airfield control tower. It is in, or near to, this area that control signals are displayed.

Red square 6′ × 6′.

The special rules for air traffic in vicinity of aerodrome open to public use not in force.

Red square, yellow diagonal superimposed.

Special care necessary in landing owing to temporary obstruction or for other reason.

Red square, yellow cross superimposed.

Landing prohibited.

Red square, two parallel yellow bars superimposed.

Landings should be made with extreme caution as safety services are not available. (Displayed at R.A.F. aerodromes.)

PLATE VI

Red-and-yellow-striped arrow.

Circuits or partial circuits must be right-handed. Keep movement area on the right.

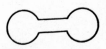

White dumb-bell.

Landings and taking off on runways only. Taxi-ing on grass prohibited.

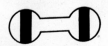

White dumb-bell with two black bars.

Landing and taking off on runways only. Taxi-ing on grass permitted.

White dumb-bell with red " L."

Light aircraft may land on special grass area. Taxi-ing on grass permitted.

White " T."

Land and take off in direction of " T."

give exhibitions, and then only with special permission. These are always experienced men, well versed in the art of aerobatics and acutely conscious of the limitations within which a pilot must work in order to aerobat in safety. The spectators, too, can be counted on as being favourable towards the exhibitions, because presumably they would not be there if they were going to complain about the noise and thrill of low flying.

Roughly speaking, aerobatics can be divided into two classes: those that do not involve inverted flying and those that do. By inverted flying I mean flying in which for varying periods the machine is actually flying inverted. Looping, although the machine is upside-down at the top of a loop, does not involve inverted flying. At no time during a loop is the weight of the machine borne by the TOP surface of the wing. In inverted flying the weight of the machine is borne by the top surface of the wing.

For none of the aerobatics that come in these classifications is any special equipment necessary for pilot or engine. Indeed, a skilled aerobatic pilot can give a most comprehensive and thrilling display of aerobatics, during which his machine is frequently upside-down, without his even being held into his seat by his harness. As a precaution he would certainly be properly strapped in, but if he did his aerobatics accurately and well, his weight need never be taken off his seat, and therefore there would be no tendency for him to fall out.

D

THE LOOP

The easiest evolution to do is, strangely enough, the loop (Fig. 12). I say " strangely enough ", because ever since it was first done by a brave Frenchman in about 1912, this manœuvre has

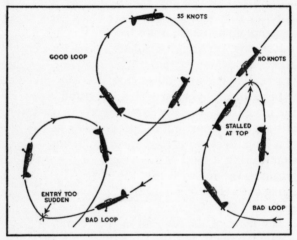

FIG. 12.—The Loop.

kept the public's fancy as the acme of aerobatics. To the layman the loop still represents the epitome of a pilot's skill and bravery. How reluctant one is, therefore, to have to admit that the loop is one of the easiest manœuvres in flying!

Before doing a loop, it is necessary to gain a little extra speed, so, after looking around you to see that there are no other aircraft in the vicinity, ease the nose down a little and give the engine three-quarter throttle. Observe and note some spot on the horizon on which you must come out of the loop, so that you may be sure of doing a straight one and finishing in exactly the same direction as that in which you started. When you have reached a speed of about 125 knots, start easing back on the control column, at the same time pushing the throttle full open so that the engine gives all its power. You want to ease the control column back gently but firmly. As you are going fast more pressure will be required; and you will also find that the comparatively sudden change of direction to which you are subjecting the machine results in a strong application of centrifugal force that presses you hard down on your seat. It is, however, by the feel of this force that you can determine the strain to which you are subjecting the machine. Experience will tell you just to what degree the control column should be eased back. As the machine mounts up and over it obviously loses speed rapidly, and this in turn reduces the effect of the controls. As you go up you continue easing back the control column until, when you are upside-down at the top of the loop, it is as far back in your stomach as it can go. At this point close the throttle and keep the control column back until the nose drops and the speed increases, then ease it forward as necessary and level off from the resultant dive. When you are flying level you can open up the engine again. When in the dive care must be taken not to get excessive engine speed.

It is easy to do a slovenly loop, but, like everything else in flying, much practice and concentration are required before you can do a neat one: one that is perfectly smooth to the onlooker with no " corners " and which does not suffer from a crooked path or dipped wing at the top of the loop. In fact, the rudder plays as important a part in the loop as the elevator.

If you do not judge a loop properly, one of two things may happen. By pulling back on the control column roughly and too quickly you will strain the machine, besides making it extremely uncomfortable for yourself, and if you are too timid and do not ease back enough you will " hang " on top of the loop and stall when inverted. You have to judge it so that you maintain flying speed all the time. Obviously, if you take too long over the steep climb on the first half of the loop you will lose flying speed. If you are upside-down when you do this you will leave your seat, because it is centrifugal force that keeps you in, and that depends on the rate of change of direction. You can swing a bucket full of water around your head without spilling a drop, so long as you swing it fast enough; but if you swing it too slowly all the water will fall out as soon as the bucket is inverted. Exactly the same thing happens in a looping aeroplane.

STALLED TURN

A stalled turn is an easy manœuvre to do, and graceful to watch. Fly along level, and ease the

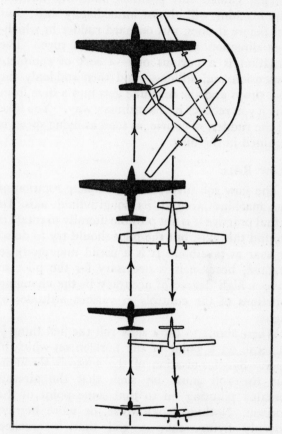

FIG. 13.—A Stalled Turn.

nose up until it is pointing vertically into the air. Having gained this position, shut the throttle. The machine will almost immediately stall; but just before it does, put on hard rudder in whichever direction you wish to do the turn. The sensation is a curious one—a sort of complete suspension and stillness—and then suddenly the nose drops and the machine gets into a dive from which you recover in the ordinary way. You take off the rudder, of course, as soon as flying speed is regained in the dive.

SLOW ROLL

The slow roll involves the complete rotation of the machine around its longitudinal axis. In actual practice it is not possible literally to rotate it around this axis, but the pilot should try to do so as near as possible. It is a useful manœuvre to practise, because it is necessary for the pilot to have a high degree of accuracy in the changing functions of the controls in various attitudes of flight.

When about to do a slow roll the first thing is to settle on a point of the horizon on which to steer. Synchronisation of the controls throughout the roll must be such that the aircraft remains pointing on to that same point of the horizon. Nothing looks worse, or more betrays slovenly flying, than a roll that is crooked (Fig. 14).

Having chosen your point (by the way, a roll always looks more effective from the ground if it is done down-wind), ease the nose down to gain a little speed. 110 knots is enough. Then ease back on the stick until the nose is above the horizon, and at the same time, if you are rolling to the right, ease the control column over to the right-hand side of the cockpit. This must be done firmly, because the ailerons will offer a fair amount of resistance at this speed. The machine will then immediately start to bank to the right. Adjust the rudder so that it remains straight. As soon as a fair amount of bank has been put on the nose will

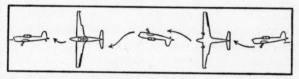

FIG. 14.—A Slow Roll.

start to drop. This must be counteracted by top rudder. When the machine is vertically on its side the elevator becomes entirely responsible for keeping it straight (as in a vertically banked turn). The control column has therefore to be eased forward to prevent the machine turning to the right; at the same time it is kept in the right side of the cockpit in order to continue the roll. As the machine gets on to its back, close the throttle and keep the control column forward in order to keep the nose above the horizon. This forward movement of the control column is gradually taken off as the machine rolls off its back, and again top rudder has to be applied to keep the nose just above the horizon. As you get past the vertical position, take off the rudder as necessary and gently open the throttle, so judging it that the controls are once again centralised and the engine is running normally at the moment of resuming level flight. It is easy to get into the habit of rolling one way only. Do not allow this to happen. Give yourself equal opportunity to roll to the left.

HALF-ROLL OFF THE TOP OF A LOOP

This manœuvre is a useful one for changing direction and at the same time gaining height. Its name is self-explanatory—the first half of a loop followed by the second half of a slow roll (Fig. 15).

In order that ample flying speed is in hand at the top of the loop to enable the controls to operate successfully, it is necessary to start this manœuvre with more speed than is necessary for a loop. Ease the nose well down and get up to a speed of about 140 knots. Then gently ease the control column back as though you are going to execute a loop. When the machine is on its back ease the control column forward to prevent the nose dropping, at the same time easing it to whichever side you are going to roll off. As usual, the nose must be kept straight with a combination of rudder and elevator.

When executing this manœuvre a good point to remember is to watch for the horizon as you come over the top of the loop and commence the roll off just before the nose reaches the horizon, otherwise height will be lost instead of gained.

To wind up this chapter on aerobatics, I am going to quote from an article written by the champion pilot of the Netherlands for 1937. It is

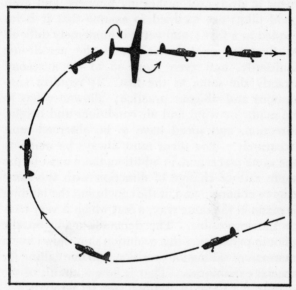

FIG. 15.—Half-roll off the Top of a Loop.

an admirable note on the art of aerobatic flying, and I am indebted to *Shell Aviation News* for permission to reproduce it.

" The idea that aerobatics are beyond the capabilities of the ordinary pilot is a misconception based on the fact that only the expert does them in public. They should be just as much a part of the training of a pilot as the more simple manœuvres, for they are fundamentally the same thing.

" Aerobatics begin with a perfectly flown circuit of the aerodrome. Whenever I make this statement it always astonishes my listeners, and even good pilots are inclined to assume that it is intended as a joke; and yet it is immensely difficult to fly even one circuit round the aerodrome faultlessly, and even more so to do a second exactly the same as the first. It requires continuous and diligent practice; allowance has to be made for wind and air conditions and height, direction, and speed have to be observed most accurately. The turns must always be made at the same place, and, in addition, there must be the same rate of change of direction with the same degree of bank; and at the conclusion the landing is made in the same way, a feat which is very near to the impossible. The demands made on the pilot in performing this evolution show how close a manœuvre calling for precision is to one calling for special capabilities. That is how a circuit of the aerodrome becomes the first step in aerobatics.

" I have demonstrated how accuracy in flying is a feature of aerobatics; a further one is the acquisition of perfect control over the aircraft in whatever position it is. While accuracy is a matter for our senses and understanding, this is a matter of mentality. Aerobatics train us to develop the mentality to meet the serious incidents in flying, and are not an end in themselves. In the event of trouble developing in flight, the trained and experienced aerobatic pilot will make the right decision quickly and calmly. He brings his aircraft back from any undesired and unusual flying attitude to the normal in the shortest possible time and with as little strain on it as possible. He is familiar with all attitudes, flying conditions, and movements, and knows how to change from one to the other. His aerobatic training enables him to appreciate a situation quickly.

"When he becomes a pilot, a man enters an element which is unfamiliar—he knows land and water, but not air. None of his ancestors have been up in the air, and he lacks the inherited sense which makes things easy for him elsewhere. He lacks the senses of a bird, and is not familiar with air space and the phenomena which he meets there such as sudden changes in altitude and speed. Enormous centrifugal forces, for example, which are not encountered elsewhere, may be encountered for the first time; the whole rhythm of existence in the air is different from that on the ground.

"Sometimes even during a quite ordinary flight something develops which is far from ordinary, and in aerobatic flying this may be, to say the least of it, queer; for the laws of Nature as we know them seem to have been turned topsy-turvy. Normally one falls downwards towards the earth: is it not extraordinary, then, that one should be, under certain conditions, impelled upwards, away

from the aircraft and towards the sky? And
then often it is amazingly difficult to stretch an
arm or hand downwards in the direction of the
earth. Our blood, too, is subject to physical
laws, and is affected by the centrifugal and
centripetal forces. As it is a very component
substance of the human body, these effects are of
supreme importance. Our senses can only work
as long as they are fed. by the blood, and in
aerobatic flying shortage or excess may occur in
any of our various organs, depending on the
course the aerobatic figures and movements take,
and the pressures and forces they involve. In-
sufficiently supplied with blood, our organs refuse
to work; if the blood is kept away from the brain
by centrifugal force, we lose our faculty of thinking
and our consciousness. Before that stage is
reached, however, we lose slowly our faculty for
seeing, and this is always the signal for us to
allow the blood to return to the brain; this is
easily done by a slight movement of the controls,
provided the body is well rested and elastic. In
the case of great bodily tiredness, which may be
caused by too much aerobatics, stronger measures
may have to be taken, because the vascular
system of the body is then so weak that it can no
longer resist. In such cases certain compensation
can be made by increasing the quantity of blood
fluid, for if the blood vessels extend, the quantity
of blood becomes relatively smaller.

" The advantages of aerobatic training cannot
be denied, but they are only to be enjoyed through

continual practice and training to overcome the mental and physical difficulties. Here a distinction may be made between practice and training, for by practice we understand the art of learning anything, and by training attaining the appropriate physical, intellectual, and mental condition for that purpose. I can master something by practice without having trained for it, but only training makes it possible for me to repeat the procedure at any time equally well. Knowledge and ability are therefore not everything, and training is of paramount importance."

GLOSSARY OF FLYING AND AERO-NAUTICAL TERMS

ABSOLUTE CEILING.—The greatest height that can be reached by an aerodyne or aerostat in Standard Atmosphere. The theoretical height at which the rate of climb is zero.

ACTION, RADIUS OF.—Half the range of an aeroplane in still air.

AEROBATICS.—Voluntary evolutions performed in the air, other than those required for normal flying.

AERODYNAMICS.—The science of the laws relating to forces acting on bodies moving in air.

AERODYNE.—A generic term for heavier-than-air aircraft, which derive their lift when flying chiefly from aerodynamic forces—aeroplanes, gyroplanes, helicopters, ornithopters, kites, or gliders.

AEROFOIL.—A surface designed to produce an aerodynamic force at approximately right angles to its direction of motion. Usually a wing, tail-plane, or fin.

AEROPLANE.—A mechanically driven heavier-than-air flying-machine which has fixed wings. An aerodyne with fixed wings. The term includes land-planes, sea-planes, and amphibians. When an aeroplane is specifically meant the word should be used in preference to the generic term "aircraft". The abbreviation "plane", commonly used, is not correct, and should be avoided. "Plane" properly means a wing.

AEROSTAT.—A generic term for aircraft that derive their lift chiefly from buoyancy in the air: lighter-than-air craft, balloons, or airships.

AILERON.—Movable aerofoil fitted near the wing-tip of an aeroplane and designed to make possible a rolling movement about the longitudinal axis. Ailerons are invariably connected differentially to the control column, so that when one is raised to depress a wing the other is lowered to raise its wing. (See also DIFFERENTIAL AILERONS.)

AIR-BRAKE.—A device, usually in the form of a flap, designed to increase the drag of an aeroplane at will. Used to steepen the glide, shorten the approach, and reduce the landing run.

AIRCRAFT.—A generic term for all types of flying-machines, both heavier than air and lighter than air.

AIRMANSHIP.—Proficiency in the knowledge of handling and operating aircraft on the ground and in the air.

AIRSCREW.—All types of screws with helical blades designed to rotate in air, and more particularly power-driven screws designed to produce thrust by rotation in the air. The term includes pushers and tractors. The term "propeller" is now more generally used. Airscrew slip is the ratio of the actual advance per revolution of an airscrew to the theoretical advance per revolution. Airscrew efficiency is an expression of this ratio, normally about 82 per cent.

AIR SPEED.—The speed of a flying-machine or

airship relative to the air, as distinct from its speed relative to the ground. Thus an aeroplane flying at 200 m.p.h. air speed against a 50-m.p.h. wind will have a ground speed of only 150 m.p.h.

AIR-SPEED INDICATOR.—An instrument which registers the speed of aircraft through the air, as distinct from relative ground speed.

AIRWORTHY.—A term used to denote that an aeroplane has been examined and passed as safe for flying. A certificate of airworthiness must be held by every British civil aeroplane.

ALTIMETER.—An instrument, usually a converted type of aneroid barometer, graduated to indicate height above a given datum, usually sealevel.

ANGLE OF ATTACK.—The angle between the chord line of an aerofoil and the relative airstream, no matter what the attitude of the aeroplane.

ANGLE OF INCIDENCE.—The angle between chord line of the wing and the centre line of an aeroplane.

ANGLE OF INCIDENCE (RIGGING).—The angle between the chord line of the mainplane of an aeroplane and the horizontal when the aeroplane is in the specified " rigging position " on the ground. It should not be confused with the True Angle of Incidence.

ARTIFICIAL HORIZON.—An instrument, operated by a gyroscope, devised to keep an indicator permanently parallel with the true horizon and thus show the pilot the attitude of his aeroplane when flying in cloud or bad visibility.

AXES.—Imaginary lines about which an aeroplane may change its attitude in flight. An aeroplane has three axes. They are:

(i) LATERAL AXIS.—The straight line through the centre of gravity parallel to a line which would join the wing-tips.

(ii) LONGITUDINAL AXIS.—The straight line through the centre of gravity parallel to a line which would join nose and tail.

(iii) NORMAL AXIS.—The straight line through the centre of gravity at right angles to the lateral axis and the longitudinal axis. When the aeroplane is flying so that the longitudinal axis and the lateral axis are horizontal the normal axis is vertical.

BALANCED SURFACES.—Control surfaces of an aeroplane (ailerons, elevators, rudder, and flaps) in which the aerodynamic movements about the hinge are wholly or partly self-balanced.

HORN BALANCE.—A small balance area at the tip of a control surface, usually projecting forward of the main surface.

MASS BALANCE.—A weight set forward of a control surface designed especially to prevent flutter.

BALANCE TAB.—A hinged area at the rear portion of a control surface designed to move in the opposite direction to the control surface and so balance it.

BANK.—The angle between the lateral axis of an aeroplane and the horizontal plane. BANKING is angular motion about the longitudinal axis of an aeroplane when turning.

BUMP.—A colloquial term used to denote any sudden vertical or lateral movement of an aeroplane caused by thermal or eddy currents or gusts. Often erroneously referred to as " air pockets ".

CAMBER.—The curvature of the surface and/or centre line of an aerofoil section which causes lift. A heavily cambered aerofoil is usually a high-lift section. A slightly cambered aerofoil is usually a high-speed section.

CARBURETTER.—A device which, with the aid of a draught of air, converts the fuel supply of an aero-motor from a fluid into a vapour which is mixed with an appropriate amount of air and introduced into the combustion chamber as an explosive mixture.

CEILING.—The maximum height to which an aeroplane can climb. The ABSOLUTE CEILING is the height at which the rate of climb is zero and at which the aeroplane has only one possible flying speed. Absolute ceiling is sometimes called the theoretical ceiling. The SERVICE CEILING is the height at which the rate of climb of any aeroplane has dropped to 100 ft. per minute, and is reached in about forty minutes by any aeroplane.

CENTRE-LINE CAMBER.—The ratio between the chord of an aerofoil and the maximum height of the centre line above the chord line. A measure of the amount of curvature between the leading and trailing edges.

CENTRE OF GRAVITY.—The point in a body through which the resultant of the weights of the parts which make up that body may be assumed to pass whatever the attitude of the body.

CENTRE OF PRESSURE.—An imaginary line along the span of an aerofoil on which all the aerodynamic forces on the aerofoil affecting lift may be assumed to act. The centre of pressure of an aerofoil is normally about one-third of the way back from the leading edge, but in certain flying attitudes and with flaps extended it may vary greatly and may even move right off the aerofoil altogether. The movement in the centre of pressure is of importance structurally as well as aerodynamically.

CHOCK.—A wedge, usually of wood, placed in front of the wheels of an aeroplane on the ground to prevent it from moving forward when the engine is run up.

CHORD.—The width of an aerofoil section, usually the wing, measured in a straight line from leading to trailing edge.

COMPASS.—An instrument which consists essentially of a magnetic needle free to swing and which, subject to correction for conflicting magnetic fields, always points to the Magnetic North. It thus indicates the angle in the horizontal plane between the Magnetic North and the longitudinal axis of the aeroplane.

COMPASS COURSE.—The angle between the longitudinal axis of an aeroplane and the compass needle, measured clockwise from the compass needle through 360 degrees.

CONSUMPTION.—The quantity of fuel or oil consumed by an aero-motor or aero-motors, defined in gallons per hour or in pints per hour.

" CONTACT ".—A colloquial term used to announce that the switch of an aero-motor is on and the pilot is ready for the motor to be started. Now largely a relic from the days when airscrews were swung by hand, and to avoid possible confusion between the words " on " and " off ".

CONTROL SURFACE.—A surface, movable in flight to control the motion of an aeroplane about its axes. The three principal control surfaces are the elevators, the rudder, and the ailerons.

COURSE.—In air navigation the direction of the horizontal longitudinal axis of an aeroplane with reference to the angle it makes with a specified datum, the track. The course is set on the verge ring of the compass, and includes both the bearing of one's destination and an allowance for the effect of wind and the consequent drift.

DEAD RECKONING.—In air navigation the estimation of true direction and speed of an aeroplane during flight, and hence of its distance from any known point at any moment.

DIFFERENTIAL AILERONS.—Ailerons interconnected so that the aileron which moves upwards moves through a larger angle than the other, which moves downwards. The reason for this is to increase the drag as well as the lift of the wing with the upgoing aileron and at the same time to keep down the drag of the downgoing aileron because of its smaller movement.

DIHEDRAL ANGLE.—The angle at which the port and starboard mainplanes, or tailplane, of an aeroplane or glider are inclined upwards to the lateral axis. When they are inclined downwards the angle is termed Anhedral or Negative Dihedral.

DIRECTIONAL-GYRO.—More properly called Direction Indicator. An instrument to indicate any change in the direction of an aeroplane. Deviation from a straight course is shown by marks along a graduated card kept at a fixed datum by a gyroscope. The graduated card can be set to coincide with the magnetic compass.

DRAG.—The total resistance of an aeroplane along its line of flight.

DRIFT.—The movement of an aeroplane in a horizontal plane through the influence of a crosswind. Drift makes necessary the deflection of the longitudinal axis of the aeroplane away from the line of track to be followed. That is to say, an aeroplane must be headed slightly towards a beam wind to avoid being drifted off its course.

DUAL CONTROL.—Flying controls which are duplicated in an aeroplane either for instruction or so that one pilot may conveniently relieve another.

ECONOMICAL CRUISING POWER.—The percentage of the maximum level horse-power of an aero-engine at which the specific consumption is the lowest.

ECONOMICAL CRUISING SPEED.—The speed at which an aeroplane achieves its greatest range in still air. This speed is usually about 85 per cent of the maximum speed.

EDGE.—(a) *Leading Edge.*—The forward edge of an aerofoil (including an airscrew blade, strut, or any streamlined body).

(b) *Trailing Edge.*—The rear edge of an aerofoil, strut, or any streamlined body, or airscrew blade.

ELEVATOR.—Control surfaces hinged to the trailing edge of the tailplane to provide longitudinal control. By raising the elevators the tail is depressed and the nose raised, and vice versa.

EMPENNAGE.—A general term, now little used, to refer to the tail unit of an aeroplane. Empennage includes tailplane, elevators, fins, and rudders.

ENDURANCE.—The maximum time that an aeroplane can continue to fly without refuelling. The speed for maximum endurance is normally about 20 per cent above the stalling speed, changing as the stalling speed varies with the constant diminution in weight caused by the burning of fuel.

FACTOR OF SAFETY.—A strength factor to which all aeroplanes are built. Thus a factor of safety of five means that any part of the aeroplane is designed to withstand five times its normal load before failing. A factor of safety of one would mean that the machine would be on the point of breaking at its normal load. Aeroplanes intended for high-speed aerobatics have a higher factor of safety than those intended for normal level flying only.

FAIRING.—A secondary structure added to reduce drag. Common examples of fairings are wing-root fillets and the streamlining of struts.

FIN.—A fixed vertical surface, usually at the tail, designed to contribute to both directional and lateral stability. Often called the " tail fin " and usually used to carry the rudder. On lighter-than-air craft the term fin is also used to define the horizontal stabilising surfaces termed the tailplane in an aeroplane.

FLAP.—A hinged surface, usually at the trailing edge of a wing, used to increase the lift of a wing at slow speeds, to steepen the glide, and to act as an air-brake during the approach and landing.

FLAP ANGLE.—The angle between the chord of the wing and the chord of the flap. Flaps are often lowered about 5 degrees to assist take-off and usually about 30 to 45 degrees for landing.

FLATTENING OUT.—In approaching to land an aeroplane, the transition from the gliding approach to the position to alight is termed " flattening out ".

FLYING POSITION.—The attitude of an aeroplane when it is flying straight and level.

FORCED LANDING.—The unpremeditated landing of an aeroplane usually caused by mechanical breakdown.

FUSELAGE.—The main body of a land-plane, sea-plane, or amphibian, providing accommodation for the crew and useful load.

GLIDE.—The gradual descent of an aeroplane with gravity alone providing the motive power.

GLIDING ANGLE.—The angle between the path of flight of an aeroplane and the horizontal while gliding.

GROUND SPEED.—The speed of an aeroplane relative to the earth's surface, as distinct from its speed through the air. Thus if an aeroplane is flying at 200 m.p.h. through the air and is flying against a steady wind of 20 m.p.h. its ground speed will be 180 m.p.h.

INDICATED AIR SPEED.—The air speed as shown by an air-speed indicator. The reading agrees with the true air speed only if atmospheric conditions are "standard". As height increases, the indicated air speed falls below the true air speed.

INSTABILITY.—The tendency of an aeroplane to depart involuntarily from the set line of flight. Instability may express itself in yawing (swinging to right or left), rolling, or porpoising (following an undulating path). Such faults may arise from a variety of causes, *e.g.*, insufficient fin area, too short a fuselage, inefficient tailplane, failure to compensate in wing or aileron adjustment for the torque (twisting tendency) of the motor.

INSTRUMENT FLYING.—The art of flying an aeroplane solely by instruments without reference to any external datum or horizon.

KNOT.—A nautical unit of speed being equal to one nautical mile (6,080 feet) per hour. To convert knots to miles per hour multiply by 1·15.

LIFT.—The component in a vertical, upward direction in straight and level flight of the resultant force created by the relative wind acting on the lifting surfaces of an aeroplane.

LONGERON.—A main longitudinal strength member of a fuselage or nacelle.

LONGITUDINAL AXIS.—A line fore and aft through the centre of gravity of an aeroplane and parallel to the line of flight.

LUBBER LINE.—A line fixed to the forward end of a compass bowl. It corresponds to the nose of the aeroplane, and enables the pilot to determine the direction in which the aeroplane is heading at any time.

MAGNETIC COURSE.—The angle (measured in a clockwise direction) between the course of an aeroplane—that is, the direction steered—and Magnetic North. It is measured on a map from the nearest magnetic meridian, or compass rose.

MILLIBAR.—The thousandth part of a bar, a bar being a unit of barometric pressure equal to 750·1 mm. (29·531 inches) of mercury at 0° C. in latitude 45 degrees.

MIXTURE CONTROL.—A device embodied in the carburetter of an aero-motor for reducing the quantity of fuel supplied to the cylinders as height increases so as to maintain a constant ratio of fuel to air.

NAVIGATION.—The science of determining and plotting the position of an aircraft and of determining the courses to steer to reach any required destination.

NAVIGATION LIGHT.—A light on an aeroplane to reveal its presence and direction of motion at night. A complete set of navigation lights comprises a red light on the port (left) wing-tip, a green light on the starboard (right) wing-tip, and a white light at the tail.

PERFORMANCE.—The essential flying characteristics of aircraft under standard atmosphere conditions. The figures obtained under any existing conditions are corrected so as to apply to a standardised theoretical state of the atmosphere.

PILOTAGE.—The art of piloting aircraft safely and accurately from one place to another by means of map-reading and the recognition of ground objects.

POSITION ERROR.—The reading of an air-speed indicator differs from the true air speed because of a number of errors. The error arising from the mounting of the Pitot tube in a position where the air flow is disturbed by its proximity to the aeroplane is termed the " position error ".

REVOLUTION INDICATOR.—An instrument which records the rate of revolution of the crankshaft of a motor in turns per minute. Sometimes known as a tachometer, and colloquially as a " rev counter "—although this latter term is, strictly speaking, inaccurate.

RUDDER.—A vertical moving surface usually hinged to the sternpost of the fin in the tail unit of an aeroplane. Its functions are to provide directional control and to assist directional stability.

RUDDER BAR.—The foot control by which the pilot of an aeroplane controls the rudder. It is hinged about its centre, and when pushed forward with the left foot yaws the nose to the left, and vice versa.

SAILPLANE.—A high-performance glider capable of soaring flight.

SKIN FRICTION.—That portion of drag which is covered by the movement of a fluid (e.g., air) over the surface of a body (e.g., aerofoil). The rougher the surface the greater the skin friction.

SLIPPING AND SKIDDING.—Movement sideways through the air from the course ahead. Slipping will occur, for example, when an aircraft is turned with too much bank and slips inwards and downwards. Skidding will occur when the aircraft is turned with too little bank and skids outwards.

SLIP-STREAM.—The stream of air behind an airscrew which usually has about 20 per cent greater speed than that of the aeroplane, at every speed.

SLOT.—A narrow air passage formed by a "slat", running spanwise on an aerofoil, flap, aileron, elevator, or rudder. A slot gives greater control at critical angles of attack, and acts on the principle of smoothing the turbulent wake and so delaying the stall of a surface.

SPAN.—The overall distance from wing-tip to wing-tip.

SPAR.—The main longitudinal beam or beams of a wing or control surface. Secondary structures are built around the spar to transfer the load to it, and in the case of wing-ribs, also to give correct aerofoil form.

STALL.—The wing of an aeroplane is said to stall when the smooth flow over the top surface breaks down and degenerates into turbulence. Reverse flow may even be present. The lift of the wing then drops suddenly and with it controllability. A dive is necessary to pick up speed and restore the flow. Most wings stall normally at 15 degrees or at 25 degrees with slots.

STREAMLINE.—A form designed to reduce resistance to motion through a fluid and to eliminate eddies. A good streamline form appears to have a longitudinal section rather like an elongated peardrop with the wider end foremost.

STRESS.—The product of the load on a body divided by the area subjected to load, usually expressed in foot-pounds per square inch. A body is in tension when the force tends to pull it apart.

It is in compression when the force tends to squeeze the body together. The change in shape caused by tension or compression is called strain.

STRESSED SKIN.—The form of aircraft construction in which the external skin carries part or all of the main loads.

STRINGER.—A secondary member of an aeroplane structure, usually running parallel to the main spars or longerons, which assist in maintaining the external form.

SUCTION.—A lowering of pressure in a confined space causing a fluid to enter, or one body to adhere to another, under atmospheric pressure.

TAILPLANE.—The fixed horizontal tail surface of an aeroplane.

TAIL WHEEL.—The small wheel which takes the weight of an aeroplane fuselage on the ground at the tail.

TAXI-ING.—Manœuvring aircraft on the ground or on water.

THRUST.—The force exerted by an airscrew along its thrust line.

TORQUE.—The moment of the aerodynamic forces about the thrust line of an airscrew which tends to turn the aeroplane in the opposite direction to that in which the airscrew is rotating.

TRACK.—A course followed by projection of the path of the centre of gravity of an aeroplane on to the surface of the earth.

TRACK ANGLE.—The angle, at any moment, between the track of an aeroplane and the meridian, measured clockwise through 360 degrees.

TRIM.—The set or angle at which an aeroplane flies under given conditions.

TRIMMING TABS.—Small auxiliary movable tabs on the trailing edges of control surfaces.

TRUE AIR SPEED.—The speed of an aeroplane through the air in which it is flying corrected for errors, *i.e.*, position error, instrument error, and error caused by height (less dense atmosphere) and temperature.

TRUE COURSE.—The angle between the longitudinal axis of an aeroplane and a true meridian.

UNDERCARRIAGE.—The main alighting gear of an aeroplane or float-plane. Modern undercarriages are usually retractable to reduce drag.

VENTURI TUBE.—A tube made with a gradually reduced cross-section about its centre which speeds up fluid flow through the tube at that point and so produces a depression.

WING.—The main lifting surface of an aeroplane.

THE GUILD OF AIR PILOTS AND AIR NAVIGATORS OF THE BRITISH EMPIRE

This Guild was founded in 1929 on the lines of the old City Guilds with rules modelled on those of the Company of Master Mariners. Entirely non-political, its main objects are to further the efficiency of mercantile flight and uphold the dignity and prestige of Air Pilots and Air Navigators, and so maintain the status of those engaged in the profession.

ROYAL PATRONAGE

In January 1947, H.R.H. The Princess Elizabeth graciously consented to become the Grand Master—so setting the seal on the Guild's integrity and seriousness of purpose.

It will be remembered that H.R.H. the late Duke of Kent had already honoured the Guild by becoming the Grand Master during the middle thirties.

MEMBERSHIP

Full Membership embraces qualified professional pilots and navigators; Service Membership—qualified Service pilots and navigators, including those who intend to adopt flying as a civil career on the termination of their Service engagement; Associate Membership—those whose qualifications do not entitle them to Full Membership. Honorary Membership is conferred on those who have rendered signal service to the objects of the Guild in especial circumstances.

In 1934 there were 275 members. Today there are over 1,500, and the number is steadily increasing. The more members there are, the more representative the Guild becomes and the more it can do.

LIAISON WORK

It acts as a link between its members and the Ministry of Civil Aviation, Ministry of Supply, Central Medical Board, Society of British Aircraft Constructors, Aircraft Operators, The Royal Aeronautical Society, Royal Aero Club, Association of British Aero Clubs, established City Companies, Parliamentary Committees, and many other bodies on all matters affecting British civil pilots and navigators.

ADMINISTRATION

Its affairs are managed by a Court of fifteen freely elected members, with two representatives from each of the Test, Service, and Associate sections.

APPROVAL OF INSTRUCTORS

The Guild's Panel of Examiners is the responsible body, authorised by the Ministry of Civil Aviation for the examination, testing, and approving of pilots for the civilian flying instructors' certificates of competency.

TEST PILOTS' INTERESTS

The great majority of approved test pilots have formed their section within its structure, and control their affairs through their own elected committee.

EMPLOYMENT

One of its most important functions is to look after the interests of those members who may require help in finding work.

It has been able to put many members in touch with suitable appointments, and now many employers prefer to obtain their personnel through the Guild.

ASSISTANCE IN DISTRESS

Through its Benevolent Fund, the Guild comes to the aid of any members, or their dependants, who are in distress.

LEGAL ADVICE

Members can obtain initial free advice on any problem concerned with their profession.

INSURANCE

The Guild is sponsor and a trustee to a Pension Scheme especially evolved for its members.

CEREMONIES

The main annual functions are the Dinner, Installation Ceremony, and Reception. These give all members the opportunity to intermingle and exchange ideas.

THE JOURNAL

This is published every other month, and is the medium of keeping members informed of the many activities of the Guild.

YOUR ENQUIRIES WILL BE WELCOMED